Pelican Books
The Dolphin: Cousin to Man

Robert Stenuit is a widely famed diver and underwater researcher. He explored the flooded caves and underground rivers of his native Belgium before taking to the sea and participating in the discovery and excavation of ancient shipwrecks. As chief diver of the Man in Sea project (headed by the American oceanologist Edwin A. Link) he became the first of the aquanauts with his unprecedented saturation dive of 24 hours spent 200 feet under the Mediterranean in 1962. Two years later he set another record by working and living in an inflatable tent 432 feet deep near the Bahamas for two days and nights. The rapid commercialization of the technique led to his becoming a manager for an underwater engineering company serving the offshore oil industry. Today Robert Stenuit is once again devoting his full time to underwater archaeology and to writing about the sea. His discovery of the *Girona* and her treasure, the first Spanish Armada wreck located in English waters, attracted considerable interest. He is the author of eleven books and many magazine articles.

Robert Stenuit

The Dolphin:
Cousin to Man

Translated from the French
by Catherine Osborne

Penguin Books

Penguin Books Ltd, Harmondsworth,
Middlesex, England
Penguin Books Inc., 7110 Ambassador Road,
Baltimore, Maryland 21207, U.S.A.
Penguin Books Australia Ltd, Ringwood,
Victoria, Australia

First published in Great Britain by Dent 1969
Published in Pelican Books 1971
Copyright © Robert Stenuit, 1968

Made and printed in Great Britain by
Cox & Wyman Ltd,
London, Reading and Fakenham
Set in Intertype Times

Contents

List of Illustrations

It was an old custom among sailors to carry about with them little Maltese lap-dogs, or Monkeys, to amuse them on the voyage; so it happened once upon a time that a man took with him a Monkey as a companion on board ship. While they were off Sunium, the famous promontory of Attica, the ship was caught in a violent storm and, being capsized, all on board were thrown in the water, and had to swim for land as best they could. And among them was the Monkey. A Dolphin saw him struggling, and, taking him for a man, went to his assistance and bore him on his back straight for shore. When they had just got opposite Piraeus, the harbour of Athens, the Dolphin asked the Monkey if he were an Athenian. 'Yes,' answered the Monkey, 'assuredly, and of one of the first families in the place.' 'Then, of course, you know Piraeus,' said the Dolphin. 'Oh yes,' said the Monkey, who thought it was the name of some distinguished citizen; 'he is one of my most intimate friends.' Indignant at so gross a deceit and falsehood, the Dolphin dived at once to the bottom, and left the lying Monkey to his fate.

Aesop, 600 B.C.

It is an offence to the Gods to hunt dolphins, and he can no longer approach the Gods to offer a sacrifice nor touch their altars with pure hands, who of his own will has been the cause of the destruction of dolphins. He makes impure even those living under his roof, because the Gods hold the massacre of the monarchs of the depths to be as execrable as the murder of a human.

Oppian, *Halieutica*, 2nd century A.D.

It shall not be lawful for any person to take or molest any dolphin in the Hokianga Harbour ... any person committing a breach of these regulations shall be liable on summary conviction to a fine not exceeding £50.

The New Zealand Gazette (Regulations, 1956)

The capture of dolphins is henceforth prohibited in all the territories of the Soviet Union. ... I believe that it will be possible to preserve the dolphins. In the interest of science, their capture should be stopped in all the oceans and seas of the world.

M. Alexander Ishkov, Minister of Fisheries of the U.S.S.R. (*Izvestia*, 1966)

Introduction
by Jon Lindbergh

I first met Robert Stenuit on Edwin Link's research vessel *Sea Diver*. Three weeks later we passed two days together in a small rubber house 430 feet below the surface off the Bahamas. Visitors soon joined us: several large groupers took up residence in the watery 'basement' of our home. I watched Stenuit swim out among them, pet them and urge them to move on when they hogged the view through his camera. He understands the creatures of the sea in a way possible only to one who has spent much of his life with them in their own element. Robert Stenuit is uniquely qualified to acquaint man, who dominates the land, with the dolphin, supreme in the sea.

In 1966 I was part of a team which spent months searching for an H-bomb lost off the coast of Spain. Since all vision is much restricted under water, we sought to replace our eyes with sonars: instruments which can be described as searchlights using sound waves instead of light. Even with man's best sonars it was bafflingly difficult to 'see' a mass of metal weighing a ton. The dolphin, too, uses sound waves for his long-range vision in the sea. His sonar, though, can track a small fish in full flight. We have much to learn from him.

The dolphin is a mammal, warm-blooded and air-breathing like ourselves, but he lives in the sea and gets around with flukes instead of feet. With effortless grace he cavorts through the water, while the onlooking diver feels clumsy and leaden. A dolphin chatters to his fellows with garrulous abandon; we men are mute under water or project rasping electronic voices. Yet the dolphin seems to have adopted man as a friend and welcomes our blundering invasion of his domain with affable humour, as this book demonstrates.

1

Graceful, Living Torpedoes

I have been a diver all my life, and an oceanaut for some time, but in the world under the sea, where men have until now disregarded their friends, I have been alone, a traveller without a guide. Only recently, for the first time, have I begun to dream of finding friends under the sea. If the dolphins will permit me to intrude I would like to earn their friendship.

Men see dolphins in terms of human types. The idea of the dolphin as bodyguard first came to my mind because of a comment by Dr David Brown of the Marineland Aquarium in California: 'They [dolphins] swim with extraordinary speed and strike the sharks on the most sensitive parts of the stomach with their hard, bony snouts. As the shark has no bony skeleton, but only cartilages, its vital organs, not protected by a thoracic cage, crush quite easily (especially the liver), and this is how dolphins do away with sharks.' When I was in Florida in 1964 dolphins were also described to me as friendly intellectuals, as comedians, as clowns, as Good Samaritans and as prima donnas. Until then I would never have described them that way. At sea, as all divers have discovered, dolphins and porpoises do not make friends easily. They will escort a boat for hours, playing about before the bow, but as soon as a diver enters the water – pfft! All gone!

I first became acquainted with tame dolphins in the Miami Seaquarium. There, in the large salt-water pool, I slipped among them, in my bathing suit, face mask and flippers. I didn't know what to expect.

A dolphin could kill a man with a blow of its snout. It could dismember him with a snap of its jaws, because it possesses a double row of strong conical teeth, eighty-eight in all, which sink in with precision. But never, absolutely never, has a dolphin or a porpoise attacked a man, even in legitimate defence, with a harpoon in its side or when, with electrodes in its skull, it has been massacred in the name of science. On the contrary, in all the legends and myths of the Greeks, Latins, Scandinavians, Hindus and Polynesians, dolphins team up with fishermen, guide sailors between the reefs that trap them, swim to the aid of the shipwrecked and help them to land, and even share in the games of children.

Descending the Seaquarium ladder, I plunged my head under the water. One look – and it was love at first sight.

The dolphins with their long pointed noses seemed to be living torpedoes – supple, speedy, graceful, moving fluidly on their white satin bellies or grey satin backs. They made a ring around me immediately, and inspected me minutely, eyeing me sideways, each with a laughing look and a big, friendly smile. The glimmer of interest which sparkled in their eyes seemed to be a human glimmer; even had I not read in books that they are man's warm-blooded cousins, I would have been convinced now. Dolphins are mammals, give birth to their children as we do and raise them within the family with loving care. They also have to rise to the surface to refill their lungs with air, just as I do with my snorkel. I know that there still exist in the skeletons of certain cetaceans small vestiges of thigh bone and tibia buried deep in the flesh or attached to the pelvic bone. I searched among the dolphins' fins and bodies for a trace of such limbs and hips, but, out of their spindles of muscle, so perfectly adapted to thrusting through the water, nothing at all protruded.

Palaeontologists generally agree that dolphins are descended from extinct land mammals, who once searched for food on the shore, then in the sea, and finally evolved to the point of living permanently in the water. To classify these animals, naturalists created the order of cetaceans. Within the sub-order Odontoceti they placed all cetaceans who possess teeth: dolphins, sperm whales, killer whales, etc. Then they created the family Delphinidae, embracing porpoises and dolphins of all kinds. The ones I found around me were specimens of *Tursiops truncatus,* or the Atlantic Dolphin. They were of all ages – mostly adults, close to six feet long, and weighing three hundred to five hundred pounds, but there were also two or three young ones, one of whom, still nursing, followed his mother like a shadow.

To break the ice I held out a bright rubber ring to the boldest teenager. He nodded his head and I threw the ring to the far end of the pool. Without a ripple he turned around, shot off like an arrow, and came back immediately with the ring around his nose and a teasing glint in his eye. Another one signalled to me. I threw again, and all joined in the game. I then swam porpoise-style both on the surface and under water, enjoying myself like a child. I was becoming a dolphin. I photographed them from all angles, and they smiled at the lens and seemed to say 'cheese'.

Soon I tired of throwing the ring. While one dolphin distracted my attention, a young male shot up behind my back and delicately grabbed it out of my hands. The ring in its teeth, this young joker challenged me. He let me come almost near enough to catch him, then withdrew and plunged. When I accelerated, he accelerated. When I held out my arms, he turned his head. When I moved towards him, he darted away at the last moment, then stopped dead. When I had to surface, exhausted and breathless, he also emerged and exploded in a loud belly laugh.

By now I had received the message. I was no longer playing with them, they were toying with me . . .

A year and a half later I returned to the Seaquarium.

Leaning on the edge of the pool, I looked at my friends. I recognized almost all of them, this one from memory, that one from my photos. The suckling had grown up, but he still followed his mother. The young joker was almost adult. He looked at me for a long time, standing up, paddling his tail, his head high above water, his mouth half open, and his eye fixed upon me. Then, ignoring all other visitors, he went for the same rubber ring with which we had played. He looped it around his

15

nose, swam towards me and, with a twist of the neck and a hop, he threw it right in my hands. He laughed. I threw it back, and we picked up our game as if we had left it only yesterday.

In all my life I have never been so touched. For I was sure, incredible as it seems, that after a year and a half, from a vast number of visitors, my friend the dolphin had recognized me.

2   Friend of Gods, Children and Men

Other humans and other dolphins were friends in other times, if we are to believe the classical legends.

There was Taras, for example, a demigod, son of Poseidon, saved from the briny deep by a dolphin who brought him to shore. Where Taras landed he built a town which he named Tarentum (now Taranto) after himself, and when the Tarentines issued coins they engraved in the silver a picture of their legendary founder riding his dolphin.

Then there was Telemachos, son of Ulysses, who fell into the sea when an infant, before he could swim – a dolphin rescued him and carried him to shore. Ulysses, in gratitude, had the image of a dolphin carved on his signet-ring and engraved on his shield. Plutarch tells us the story. Of course, Plutarch did not write his celebrated treatise *On the Intelligence of Animals* until many centuries after the time of Ulysses, but he cites many cases before concluding: 'Of all land animals, some avoid man, and some of those who approach him, like the dog, the horse or the elephant, are loving to him because he feeds them. But on the dolphin, alone among all others, nature has bestowed this gift which the greatest philosophers long for: disinterested friendship. It has no need of any man, yet is the friend of all men, and has often given them great aid.'

Aesop already knew about dolphins' friendship with man when he wrote the fable, 'The Monkey and the Dolphin'. It went without saying: if a castaway is struggling in the water, and suddenly a dolphin appears, the castaway is brought to land, safe and sound, by the dolphin.

That is exactly what happened to Aesop's contemporary, Arion, a celebrity, creator of the dithyramb. The historian Herodotus tells the story. It seems that Arion, a native of the island of Lesbos, had gone to Corinth, to the court of Periander, to win fame and fortune. After becoming a top entertainer, he started a tour of the Greek colonies in Italy and Sicily. At the Festival of Sicily (something like an Olympic Games of the vocal arts) he reaped all the prizes, and from that day on everyone wanted to hear him. Finally, loaded with money, trophies and gold prizes, the poet chartered a Corinthian vessel in Tarentum, to take him back home to Lesbos.

In the middle of the journey came unexpected drama. The crew, maddened by the thought of all the gold on board, brutally gave him an ultimatum: 'If you want to be buried in the land of your fathers, you must die immediately, by your own hand. If not, we will throw you into the sea.'

Arion hesitated, then asked for one thing: to sing one more time, wearing his best costume. With this wish granted, and with the delighted pirates for an audience, the poet tuned his lyre and began to sing an orthian hymn, a long sacred song, very high-pitched in tone.

So beautiful was his music that a dolphin swimming near by was entranced, and when Arion jumped overboard, taking the pirates by surprise, the dolphin took him on its back and carried him to shore at Cape Tainaron (today Cape Matapan). The pirates on their arrival in port were captured, and Arion, in gratitude, offered a bronze votive figure of himself astride his dolphin to the temple of Tainaron.

Fiction? Herodotus heard the story two centuries later at Lesbos, confirmed it at Corinth, and he himself went to the sanctuary at Cape Tainaron, where, he tells us, he saw with his own eyes the little bronze votive offering. The same story is confirmed by eighteen Greek and seventeen Latin authors (most of whom, however, just plagiarize each other).

Next there was Korianos, a friend of dolphins, whose adventure Plutarch (quoting Phylarchos) tells: some fishermen of Byzantium had captured a group of dolphins in their net and were preparing to kill them. Korianos, a mortal, a native of

Paros, who happened to be there, intervened. He pleaded for their lives, paid the fishermen, freed the dolphins from the nets and carried them back to the water. The dolphins looked at him for a long time, then dived and disappeared. Some time after that, off the coast of Naxos, a storm overtook a boat in which Korianos was travelling. He alone among all the passengers escaped – because a dolphin found him and carried him to shore. He landed in the grotto of Sycinus, which was afterwards named 'the grotto of Korianos'. In conclusion, Plutarch says: 'When Korianos died, as the smoke from his funeral pyre rose along the seashore, a silent group of dolphins assembled, heads above water, to join the mourners. When the smoke died down, they all disappeared, and none of them ever returned.'

At Iasos there lived a youth named Dionysos, who used to run down to the beach every day as soon as school ended. One day as he was playing in the sea a dolphin came near, made friends with him and rubbed amiably against him. The boy, frightened at first, grew braver little by little. As he became more confident, he returned the friendly attentions, and soon became the cetacean's playmate. One evening the dolphin, passing between Dionysos's legs, heaved him up on to its back, and took him away for a frolic at sea. To be towed or carried along by his friend became the boy's daily game, and each afternoon as soon as school closed, they would arrive for their rendezvous at the beach, the young man coming down from the hill, the dolphin coming out of the sea.

'All the Iasbanians came in a crowd to view with their own eyes such an extraordinary marvel,' wrote Athenaios, from whom I took the story.

One day the dolphin tried to follow his friend too far, was stranded on the beach and died.

When Alexander the Great learned of this he saw in it evidence of the great esteem in which the god of the sea, Poseidon, held Dionysos, for he believed that dolphins were the children of the gods. So the king named Dionysos Great Priest of Poseidon in the Temple of Babylon when he established the capital of his Asian empire there.

Pliny the Elder heard two similar stories (*Naturalis Historia,* ix, 8). Another child of Iasos, Hermias, also made friends with a dolphin who carried him pick-a-back. But one day a sudden squall knocked Hermias down, and he was drowned before his companion could help him. The desperate dolphin brought the body on to the sandy beach and there lay down to die. The people of Iasos concluded that the animal, feeling responsible for the child's death, had decided to share his fate. In memory of this event, they also engraved their coins with the image of the boy on the dolphin.

The other story which Pliny the Elder tells happened during the reign of Augustus. While Pliny did not see it himself, he says: 'I should be truly ashamed to tell this story, if the thing had not been attested to in writing in the works of Maecenas, Fabian, Flavius Alfius and many others.'

To go to school in Puteoli (now called Pozzuoli), on the Bay of Naples, the son of a poor fisherman had to walk every day all around Lake Lucrine, actually a gulf abounding in fish, closed by a dam. A dolphin lived in the lake, and when the child reached the near shore and called to him 'Simo! Simo!' (Simo, meaning snub-nosed in Greek, was a traditional nickname for dolphins), the dolphin would come to him no matter how far away he was. Soon they overcame any fear they might have had of each other. Day after day the child entered the water, got on Simo's back, and rode straight across the lake to school. In the afternoon the dolphin carried him home. 'And this continued for several years; then the child died of a malady, but the dolphin kept coming to wait for him, always in the same place, with an air of great sadness, and showing all the signs of the deepest affliction, until finally he died, of grief and regret.'

A number of similar cases can be found. One occurred in the Gulf of Corinth near Naupaktos, and it is the very serious philosopher Theophrastus who relates it. Another happened at Tarentum, where dolphins have always been held in high esteem. A third is referred to in a letter written in A.D. 109 by Pliny the Younger (nephew of the Elder) to his friend Caninius: 'The man who told me this', Pliny starts by stating,

is entirely trustworthy, although you scarcely care about that, being a poet, but you could trust his word, were you writing a history. The citizens of Hippo (a Roman colony near Bizerta, in Tunisia have a great fondness for fishing, sailing and swimming, especially the children. . . . During a swim towards the open sea . . . one of them . . . goes far away from the shore. Suddenly a dolphin approaches, swims in front, raises him to its back then shakes him off. Then it dives again and, to the boy's horror, takes him away out to sea. But soon it makes a half-turn and carries him back to his companions on the shore. . . . The story went around, and next day, when the children were swimming . . . the dolphin appeared again and came up to the boy, but he fled with the rest. Then, as if to call out to them, the dolphin leapt high above the water, then dived back only to burst forth again from the waves, frisking about and twisting its body into an S. It played the same game the next day, and the following days until the young men of Hippo, who had been born and raised by the sea, became ashamed of their fears. They approached the creature, called to it and played with it. They stroked the dolphin, who encouraged them. . . . The child who had established first contact swam by its side, climbed on its back, and made it pull him through the water. When he felt that the dolphin loved him, he loved it in return, and there was no more fear on either side; the child's confidence grew as he became accustomed to the animal . . . the remarkable thing is that another dolphin also accompanied them, but only as a spectator. He neither joined in their games nor accepted any familiarities; he was content to escort his mate as the boys escorted their friend . . .

Pliny was not the only one to tell this story. People came from far away to see the miraculous dolphin of Hippo. He had official recognition. One day, as he came to roll on the sand and to follow his playmates, the proconsul Flavianus anointed the dolphin's body with precious oils and unguents, a treatment usually reserved for statues of the gods. The dolphin seems not to have appreciated the experience because 'he did not appear for several days and when he returned . . . he appeared ill and languid'.

He recovered quickly, however, and resumed his games, but he had now become so famous that he attracted to Hippo all the intellectuals, officials and V.I.P.s of the proconsulate. The official visitors of course all had to be received, fed and entertained with public funds. Finally, the city taxpayers, fed up with the costly comings and goings, saw themselves approaching financial ruin and secretly had the dolphin put to death.

Fifty years later, the historian Pausanias in his *Description of Greece*, written after a visit to the little island of Porosolene, next to Lesbos, off the coast of Asia Minor, stated: 'I have seen with my own eyes, at Porosolene, a dolphin, filled with gratitude towards a child who had saved his life; he had been wounded by fishermen and the child had taken care of him. I have seen this dolphin answer the child's call and carry him on its back wheresoever the child wishes to be taken.'

About A.D. 200, Oppian, in his long poem *Halieutica*, told the same story, but with a thousand details.

This happened, not in times gone by, but in our generation. A child and a dolphin, living in the port of Porosolene, had grown up together, bound ever more strongly each year in brotherly love. When they reached the flower of their youth, the boy won first place among all the young men on land, and the dolphin surpassed all the fish in the sea. ... The young man used to launch his boat and row to the middle of the bay. He would call the animal by the name he had given him in earliest childhood. The dolphin, hearing the name, would ride the waves, swimming toward the familiar boat, his tail waving, his head proudly erect, filled with joy at seeing his friend, who would stroke him tenderly as he greeted him. It seemed as if the dolphin wanted to jump into the boat to be closer to the young man. But when the boy dived into the brine the dolphin swam next to him, side by side, and cheek by cheek, and their heads touched. ... The boy often passed his hand over his friend's neck and climbed upon his damp back, and, with happy understanding, the dolphin took the boy on his back and went wherever the child's whim directed him. ... And he not only carried his friend but also whomsoever the child brought to him, and obeyed them ... for the love of him.

Similar friendships are reported in Alexandria; in Archaea; among the Amphilochians, in Ios; at Dicaearchia, also at Paros; and in Libya, where a young shepherd is the hero.

Cicero believed the stories, for he said in his *Tusculanes*: 'A sailor, being pursued by pirates, to whom a God will say, "throw yourself overboard, a dolphin is there to rescue you, like the dolphin of Arion," will be reassured.' And Cicero – this is serious stuff, after all!

It was not only in play that dolphins helped men, but also in death. Hesiod and several others tell us of dolphins who brought back to shore the body of a man, murdered and thrown into the sea. Symeon Metaphrastes describes how a dolphin brought back to the beach of Nicomedia the martyred body of St Lucian of Antioch: '. . . And it was a very great wonder to see how the corpse rested on such a round and slippery body.'

Should one believe my Greek and Roman predecessors, even the poets along with the naturalists and historians? Is there some element of truth in the legends cited here?

Jean de La Fontaine would not believe the legends when he made his very free translation of Aesop's celebrated fable of the monkey and the dolphin. In the seventeenth century, with unveiled irony, he wrote:

> This animal is man's great friend
> Says Pliny, and ye know –
> That if his history says it –
> Why then, it must be so!

In the schoolbook where, as a child, I discovered this fable, some editor, more learned than imaginative, had put in a footnote: 'This belief is superstition, hence the pleasant irony of the storyteller.'

The Reverend Mr Bingley, an active member of the Linnean Society of London, did not believe the legends either, when he wrote, in 1802, much less pleasantly: 'How those absurd tales originated, it is impossible even to conjecture, as dolphins certainly exhibit no marks of particular attachment to mankind. If they attend a vessel navigating the ocean, it is in the expectation of plunder, and not of rendering assistance in case of distress.' And in the nineteenth century the great zoologist Brehm wrote, without wasting any time: 'The fact is that these legends are without scientific foundation.'

However, they have a remarkably durable life, these absurd

legends. Why, until the Renaissance, did the Levantine nations consider it 'a cruel and abominable thing' to insult a dolphin? Why did people of the Mediterranean, the Black Sea and the Adriatic consider it a burden on their conscience if they killed a dolphin? Belon, the French naturalist, tells why:

There is not one among them who cannot tell the tale of Arion as if it was a thing of our day.... For dolphins have for those who have fallen into the sea the same love which these showed unto them before they fell. Therefore, they never allow those drowned souls to be abandoned, but, stretching them across their backs, they shall bear them to shore. It is from this cause that men refrain from attacking them.

During the last war a dolphin pushed a rubber dinghy from the middle of the Pacific, on to the sand of a tiny island. Six American aviators, shot down by the Japanese, were crowded together in it. You will find the official report in *Airmen Against the Sea* by George Llano.

It is a fact that scientists take nothing for granted. That is why I now want to quote a scientist. Frédéric Cuvier, brother of the great Cuvier, said at the beginning of the nineteenth century:

Dolphins have not yet been the subject here with us of any observation worth mentioning or of any reported modern experiment. ... We are obliged to turn for information to Antiquity. Not all the reports have the pure ring of truth; stories of the animal are not the result of special study. They are the fruit of an unenlightened imagination which prejudice carries astray, but imagination in these stories has not invented everything. It is based upon actual facts, exaggerated no doubt, and falsely interpreted ...

It is Frédéric Cuvier again, expressing an honest, open-minded opinion, who proves to have been the first to understand that there is no possible friendship, or understanding, without strong personal contact:

If the role which dolphins played in mythology served to lead the ancients astray, it also served to help them in the observations they made of these animals; in this respect they had a factual advantage over us. Dolphins, for modern seamen, are nothing but animals covered with thick layers of blubber, and sought after for com-

24

merce. For the Greeks, they were, in certain cases, almost sacred beings, and sometimes messengers of the gods: Apollo took the form of a dolphin. As soon as our fishermen see one, they hurry to harpoon him and put him to death. When dolphins were met by the sailors of old, they were respected as harbingers of good fortune, and it was almost a sacrilege to kill them. The result of this difference in the concept of dolphins is that in ancient times, several of these animals may have become familiar with certain coasts, lingered in certain bays, even penetrated into ports, where they were received with hospitality and where, perhaps, they would take up their abode. It is the least that one can conclude from these recitals if one subtracts from them what is too obviously the stuff of fables. One can even go as far as believing that these animals are capable of contracting a degree of familiarity with the men they see habitually, and that they may become attached to them, recognize their voice, and obey them.

Inevitably, it was to men who live by the sea, with the sea, on the sea, that dolphins made the most advances – to children particularly, to children of the Mediterranean, who have the time and inclination to play with them in the warm, clear water, the boldness to follow them and a mind still free enough to accept naturally the friendship candidly offered to them.

Now, in our time, there is a return to the sea, to swimming, diving and sailing; the beaches are covered afresh with athletes and many of the conditions of ancient Greece have been restored.

The American magazine, *Natural History*, published the following story in 1949: the wife of a lawyer, a cultured and reliable person, was swimming off a Florida beach. Suddenly, a series of rollers made her lose her balance. She struggled but was carried out by a wave, swallowed water and felt she was drowning. Then, she says, 'Someone pushed me violently from behind and I landed on the beach with my nose in the sand, too exhausted to look around. When I was able to do so, there was no one near me, but in the water, twenty feet from the shore, a dolphin was jumping and swimming in circles. . . . A man came running over to me. He said, when he arrived, that I looked like a corpse, and that a dolphin had pushed me to shore.'

In March 1960, Nassau and Miami newspapers published the

story of a certain Mrs Yvonne Bliss of Florida. This fifty-year-old lady had fallen from a ship in the Bahama Channel, on the night of 29 February, without anyone on board noticing her disappearance. She swam for a long time, somehow or other, this way and that, when suddenly a dark shape appeared next to her. A shark, she thought. She swerved in terror, swimming to the right. Something touched her left hip. Then she recognized it was a dolphin, and realized that while swimming to the right she was being carried by the current, no longer taking each wave full in the face, and no longer swallowing water. The dolphin continued to escort her. 'Later,' she relates, 'he swam behind me and placed himself on my right. I swerved to make room for him. I understood only later that if the dolphin had not helped me, I would have continued to drift in the current towards the deepest, roughest waters. In fact, the dolphin guided me towards the shallowest part. Soon my feet touched bottom. When I arrived on dry land, my rescuer darted off like an arrow.'

Sally Stone, a thirteen-year-old American, was spending her vacation on the shore of Long Island Sound in 1945. Her great pleasure, with two or three friends, was to have herself towed in the water behind a sailing boat. One day a group of dolphins approached her to join the game. Sally, far from frightened, accepted their friendship. They accompanied her, gave her many love taps and did not leave her until the boat returned to port that evening. The next day, they were there again, inviting her to follow them, jumping and diving ceaselessly, to teach her, it seemed, to dive and shoot up above the water like them. Sally swam like a fish. With a dolphin on each side and a third one in front to guide her, the game went on day after day, with jumps, dashing in circles and affectionate nuzzling. Each evening the whole troupe of dolphins would follow the boat to port; one where ordinarily no dolphin would ever be seen. The summer ended, and Sally returned home.

The next year she came back to the same place for her vacation, and there, the very first day, the same six dolphins were waiting for her, recognized her and picked up the game at the very point where they had left it.

Becoming more and more intimate, girl and dolphins exchanged embraces and caresses. Sally would take hold of the back fin of one of her friends. Yielding gladly, he would swim in a circle, drawing her slowly along. It was at the insistence of biologist John Clarke that Sally Stone, years later, wrote about her adventure. But how many other girls and boys throughout the world have had similar experiences without ever telling interested adults about it?

The adventure of Sally, who had never read Plutarch or Pliny, delighted me, for it proved several things. It proved that the Greeks and Romans had not written nonsense. The thing which most charmed and moved me in this story was the similarity between Sally's dolphins and my young joker of Miami, who, at a glance, could recognize after a year's interval a land-dwelling companion, could remember the games played together and pick up their friendship exactly where they had left it.

Life magazine, too, published a dolphin story which a knowledgeable reader might at first have believed to be translated from the classics. But the dolphin is not called Simo, but Opo; it did not take place in Greece or Asia Minor, but at Opononi, a popular beach of New Zealand, in the bay of Hokianga; and the date was not 200 B.C. but A.D. 1956.

Unusually affable, even for a dolphin, Opo, who had approached the beach earlier in the season, began to frolic with a group of swimmers and was soon making daily visits to the resort. Opo proved particularly fond of the children. Swimming in close to the shore, she would wait for one of them to climb up on her back, then take off on a ride which usually ended in a friendly dunking. When the youngsters gathered for water games, Opo swam up and joined in the play. Opo spent as many as six hours a day enjoying herself at the beach; other hours were devoted to seeking food in the quiet bays along the coast.

Toward the end of the season, Opo became stranded on the rocks as the tide ran out. [This, I believe, is highly improbable – the corpse of the dolphin already dead from some other cause must have been washed ashore, for it would never have been trapped if alive.] Opononi went into mourning. All the stores closed for the day, and flags were lowered at half-mast. Solemnly Opo was buried next to the Old Soldiers' Home and a New Zealand artist began

27

sketches for a monument to commemorate the friendly dolphin of Opononi's beaches ...

The New Zealand Tourist Office confirmed the facts, and kindly sent me a series of photographs of Opo with her playmates. A New Zealand writer, Antony Alpers, took a deep interest in Opo after her death and conducted a long inquiry on the spot. He learned that the dolphin had first appeared in 1955, that it was a young female Tursiops. Yachtsmen were the first to notice her because she regularly followed their boats; then someone discovered that she loved having her back scratched with an oar or a broom. Little by little she came nearer to the beach, where she quickly succeeded in taming children and adults. The beach became famous. Every week-end, two thousand tourists would line up to watch the 'gay dolphin', as they soon named her. Signs were displayed at the city limits: 'Welcome to Opononi but don't shoot our gay dolphin.' Parking areas soon were filled with cars and traffic jams in town became a nightmare.

Alpers interviewed a girl, Jill Baker, who was then thirteen and counted herself the dolphin's best friend. Here is her story:

The dolphin became so friendly with me because I was gentle with her and never rushed at her as so many bathers did. No matter how many went in the water playing with her, as soon as I went in for a swim she would leave all the others and go off side by side with me ... on several occasions, when I was standing in the water with my legs apart she would go between them and pick me up and carry me a short distance before dropping me again. At first she didn't like the feel of my hands and would dart away, but after a while when she realized that I would not harm her she would come up to me to be rubbed and patted. She would quite often let me put little children on her back ...

Other witnesses told reporters of local magazines how extraordinarily adept Opo was at playing ball. Some bemused visitors even went in the water fully dressed just to touch her.

The gay dolphin was so famous by now that the New Zealand Government let itself be persuaded, by unanimous request, to give her legal protection. In March 1956, the *New*

28

Zealand Gazette made it officially known that: 'It shall not be lawful for any person to capture or molest any dolphin in the Hokianga Harbour. . .'

Alas, Opo was to die on that very day – her body was found on a near-by rocky shore where the outgoing tide left it. Her death remains unexplained.

It was not the first time in New Zealand history that the law had been extended to protect a cetacean. On 26 September 1904 Governor Plunket had put his seal and signature on an Order in Council whose main regulations were: '(1) During the period of five years from the date of the gazetting of these regulations, it shall not be lawful for any person to take the fish or mammal of the species commonly known as Risso's dolphin (*Grampus griseus*) in the waters of Cook Strait or of the bays, sounds and estuaries adjacent thereto. (2) Any person committing a breach of this regulation shall be liable to a penalty of not less than five pounds.' This was a handy interpretation of the laws on fisheries with a view to protect a dolphin known as Pelorus Jack. Pelorus Jack had so been christened because he dwelt in the waters of Pelorus Sound. He was a *Grampus griseus*, a thickset, whitish beakless dolphin.

For over twenty-four years, from 1888 to 1912, he faithfully escorted ships ferrying passengers across Cook Strait, between Wellington and Nelson. He had his own well-defined beat and he would take up his duties at one end of it to relinquish them only at the other end. He never missed a boat. He was always alone and would either play in front of the stem where the bow-wave pushed him effortlessly or go under to scratch his back on the ship's bottom.

Sailors were especially fond of him; travellers would come from far away and make the crossings just to see and photograph him; popular songs, postcards, labels on products and press articles made his name famous the world over.

In the eyes of the Maoris, however, Pelorus Jack's actions were nothing to be surprised at. Many generations before white men set foot on their islands a Maori by the name of Ruru had caused the death of a dolphin by uttering some forbidden malediction. The sorcerer of the tribe sentenced him to live for ever in the very body of the dolphin he had killed and to dwell near the same coast for the whole of eternity, meeting every canoe that passed. Steamships have replaced canoes nowadays, but eternity will always be eternity.

It is not by coincidence that both stories came from New Zealand. Like all peoples of the Pacific (or the Mediterranean) the Maoris are sea-goers. Like them all, they often dive and swim in the clear warm waters. Like them all they have crossed their ocean back and forth in their outriggers generation after generation. Like them all, they have lived with dolphins constantly and their mythologies accord them the same privileged place as Greek mythology.

For the Maoris dolphins are the Taniwha, the benevolent demi-gods of the seas (so Antony Alpers tells us), and just as Delphis used to rescue and guide the ancients of the Mediterranean, the Taniwha used to rescue and guide the ancients of the Pacific. Taniwha dash to the rescue of 'canoe-wrecked' fishermen; they pilot the balsa-rafts through the immensity of the oceans, all the way to the faraway atolls, and carry exhausted swimmers on their backs.

In the Pacific isles it is not Arion any more whom the 'bad guys' throw overboard, it is Te Whare; but it is a dolphin, of course, which takes him safely ashore, not at Cape Tenare, but at Maungakie-Kie. It is not the Baiae schoolboy who commutes on a dolphin's back, but the wicked sorcerer Kae or the young magician Te Tahi, of the Ngatawia tribe, and when Te Tahi dies the dolphins come and take away his corpse. They change him into one of their own kind and put him in special charge of their high-seas rescue service for shipwrecked humans.

Today, again, in other isles, thanks to the cinema and television, the marvellous story of the dolphin, friend of gods, children and men, has become a weekly miracle. The 'Flipper' series on television, seen on screens all over the world, has a dolphin star (by courtesy of Metro-Goldwyn-Mayer). Actually the series is only a marine remake of the 'Lassie' series, shot underwater to appear 'in the swim'. It describes the adventures of young Luke Halpin, who rides his playmate, Flipper, among the Florida reefs. The 'bad guys' are always the losers and the end is always the same (and the beginning too and also all vicissitudes in between).

Agreed, the role assigned the dolphin more accurately reflects the intellectual level of the script writer or that of the average television fan that that of the average odontocete. None the less, sandwiched as they are between a commercial for a 'truly' miraculous super-washing powder and another for a useless food product guaranteed to be without calories, series of this sort bring into every home the living picture of a boy – dolphin friendship. Such a relationship would otherwise have remained completely beyond the imagination, in spite of all the countless reports and stories of the Greeks, the Romans and Polynesians for the last twenty-six centuries.

At least we can hope that they will help to make better known, better loved, better protected, the sensible, good, intelligent dolphin '... on which, alone among all others', as Plutarch once said, 'Nature has bestowed this gift which all the greatest philosophers seek: disinterested friendship'.

3

From the Sea to the Land, from the Land to the Sea

The scientists, industrial researchers and military experts who are now studying dolphins proceed from surprise to mystification in the course of their work. The Greeks, however, who were so much closer than we to the creatures of the sea, had no reason to be surprised by the abilities and achievements of dolphins. Once and for all they had recognized the superior qualities of these animals.

Six centuries before Christ the Homeric hymns to Dionysos had already clearly explained the origin of dolphins. Apollodoros confirmed this in 200 B.C.

One day, Dionysos, the God of Wine and Pleasure, travelling alone disguised as a young mortal, booked passage to Ikara on a Tyrrhenian boat about to sail for Naxos. During the journey, he overheard a conversation: the crew had drawn up a plan to seize him and sell him as a slave in Asia. Calling on his divine power, Dionysos transformed the oars into serpents, created a vine whose branches grew up the mast and covered the whole vessel, while from all sides the sound of a thousand flutes were heard. Terrified by these wonders, the pirates threw themselves into the sea where they would have perished if Poseidon had not turned them into dolphins and welcomed them in his Kingdom.

The poet Oppian maintained the long classical tradition which Ovid and Propertius upheld much earlier, and he concluded, two centuries after Christ (without believing it any more than we do, of course): 'And they experienced all the pleasures of the depths when, men transformed into fish, they plunged into the waves and tried their fins for the first time. But dolphins have not forgotten that they were once men and deep into their souls they retain the memory.'

The famous cup of Exekias, now preserved in the museum of Ancient Arts in Munich, is thought to illustrate the scene; the young wine god is reclining in his vine-covered boat, escorted by seven newly metamorphosed dolphins. As dolphins do not forget that they were once men, neither do they forget their benefactor and host, Poseidon, the god whose symbol is the trident. The virgin Amphitrite, promised to Poseidon, hid herself in a sea cavern to avoid an undesired marriage. The dolphins found her, betrayed her and took her to the wedding. In gratitude, Oppian tells us, Poseidon placed in the heavens the constellation of the Dolphin. You can still see its ten stars in the northern hemisphere, even with the naked eye.

Later, when the god of the waves sought, with great discretion, to seduce the exquisite Amymone, he transformed himself into a dolphin better to carry out his courtship. When he tired of his chariot, it was his pleasure to ride a dolphin. We know from Nonnus Panopolitanus that the dolphins led Aphrodite to Cyprus after she emerged from the sea. Plutarch recounts the miraculous rescue of Enalus, the lover of Metymna (the daughter of Smintheus, you may recall). The girl was to be offered in sacrifice to Amphitrite, but her lover, mad with grief, seized her in his arms and jumped with her from the top of the cliff. The dolphins, of course, were there. And Pausanias, quoted by Lucian in his *Dialogi Marini*, tells us this Corinthian legend:

The maddened Ino, clasping to her bosom the infant Melicertes, threw herself into the sea from the higher rocks of Moluria. Now, Ino had nursed Dionysos when he was a child. The god remembered, transformed her into a sea goddess, renamed her Leucothea, and beseeched the dolphins to bring the body of Melicertes back to the shore. On the banks of the Isthmus of Corinth, in the very same place that they deposited the little body, there is an altar in memory of the miracle.

Aristotle cared nothing for poetry or the private life of the dwellers on Mount Olympus. If he speaks of dolphins at length in his *De Animalium Historia* (fourth century B.C.), of which we possess only copies of copies, it is to give the first scientific, serious and complete description of them. In fact, the book contains about forty observations, almost all of them accurate, although the intellectuals of the nineteenth century ridiculed it. Looking back today at two 'errors' attributed to Aristotle, we can have the last laugh. The false notion that the water which dolphins spurt out through their airhole is water ingested along with their food occurs in a passage which, specialists now suspect, has been much altered by copyists. The other 'error' turns out to be a correct observation, as one can now verify, by observing dolphins in oceanaria at night. They sleep either like Cartesian divers, coming up to breathe or just under the surface of the water, with their blow hole awash, thus making the 'snoring sound' that we can actually hear and which was scornfully denied by last century's 'experts', writing from their libraries.

Pliny, quoting Aristotle in his *Naturalis Historia,* added an error which was picked up and embellished by most later writers; he put a sharp spine on the back of the dolphins and then went about embroidering all earlier Greek legends with this detail: 'A dolphin tenderly folded down his spine so as not to injure the young boy he was carrying and the ripper-dolphins of the Nile massacre crocodiles with a single slash of their spine.'

The Frenchman Belon, in the sixteenth century, was the first to re-establish the truth.

Aristotle understood exactly the difference between fish (the general run of sea creatures which he calls '*Ichthues*'), and whales, dolphins and porpoises which he calls 'big fish' or '*Kete*' (the word from which we derive 'cetaceans').

He knew that cetaceans breathe air, through a respiratory tube located in the forehead which leads to lungs resembling our own. He thus knew that they would drown if kept in a net too long beneath the water, but that they could live for a long time on dry land. He knew that female dolphins have two nipples and that the young dolphin follows its mother for a long time to nurse. He knew that the dolphin has no visible organ for smelling, but still possesses a remarkable sense of smell (actually a sense of taste, which in the water comes to the same thing). He knew that a dolphin when pulled on to dry land 'wails and makes a grating noise', which is quite different from what fish do, 'because this creature has a voice, since it possesses lungs and gullet, but its tongue is not agile, nor its lips, to articulate sounds'. He knew that the animal can jump so high 'that it can pass above the mast of a ship, if there happens to be one in the vicinity', and even that the dolphin plays the game of love very much as humans do. He tells us that someone once saw a dolphin supporting on the surface of the water a baby dolphin who was dead or dying (a point often verified since, but one which for a long time attracted unjustified sarcasm); and that, occasionally, groups of cetaceans will swim aground, roll on the shore and there stay to die. Why they do that, Aristotle did not know. Neither do we today.

But Aristotle, as we well know, was scarcely acquainted with dissection.

It was in France in the sixteenth century that Guillaume Rondelet and Pierre Belon first dissected cetaceans: the first scientists to do so since antiquity.

Until that time scholars had done nothing but rewrite ancient books, adding a few errors of their own here and there to each new version, which led Pierre Belon of Le Mans to say in *The Natural History of the Strange Fish of the Sea* (which was published in 1551 in Paris, by the Press of Renaud Chaudière):

Now that I have found good reason to speak about the dolphin and other fish of its kind, well knowing that it is a fish [he means a sea creature] who holds the sceptre in the sea and to whom has been given the second place on the coats of arms of France [the son of the King of France was called *Le Dauphin de France*] and that his dignity ranks highest after the fleur-de-lys, I have deliberately taken it upon myself to describe in full all its history, after conducting a thorough observation of all its parts both exterior and interior, faithfully describing all the things which must be freely described, without adding or omitting any of the things which are theirs by nature. ... But as for the present day, I believe that modern authors who have taken it upon themselves to describe the nature of animals and plants that are unfamiliar to them, are, it seems to one, on an equal plane with the singers of old songs who croon only by instinct, without knowing the science of music. Therefore I have not proposed to amuse myself with their compilations, nor with the legends they have created. ... I will refer to those important ancient authors who have written the facts I need ... for example Aristotle, since the writers of our times, who travel in the footsteps of the ancients and who have undertaken to deal with the nature of animals they have not observed, except in the books of others, borrowing as much from authors who have lied as from those who have written the truth, can say only what they have found in the words of others. For my part, I do hope that all people will be well persuaded that I have not written anything other than what I myself have seen.

Palaeontologists of today, it would be well to mention at this point, have different views from those of Hellenic poets on the origin of cetaceans. They have closely observed their habits; they have read their skeletons like open books in which they could trace evolution of their embryonic life, for in an animal's bones and foetus one can see, like the diagram of a family tree, a *résumé* of the whole history of the race.

In the dolphin's skeleton one finds four limbs, hips, an articulated neck with seven vertebrae – in short, all the equipment of a land mammal such as a dog, for example. The forelegs have been telescoped but all the joints are still there, including five complete fingers, now protected by a mitten of flesh in the form of a fin; of the hind legs nothing remains but the hips: two little bones lost in the flesh near the bony protuberances on the spine which remind us of the pelvis that was once there. (Some whales still have remnants of the femur and a few inches of tibia.) Now they are eloquent witnesses, these tiny remnants of bones on the verge of disappearing; their presence is as eloquent as the absence of a skeleton in the caudal fluke and the dorsal fin, both of which are purely aquatic parts of the cetacean's equipment in which there is nothing but fibrous tissues and fat – in other words, materials other than bone.

The conclusion of the modern evolutionist is: with typical land features on the point of disappearing and some obviously new, purely aquatic features, the cetaceans are former land mammals now adapted to their new life in a denser liquid environment.

The first researcher to show, by means of dissection, the hidden details of the dolphin's skeleton, is Belon. He explains:

As for the anatomical studies that I have described, I want to make it definitely understood that I did not do them secretly but publicly, last year, at the College of Medicine, whilst Mr Goupil read the *Dioscuri* in Greek, in the presence of many regulars and a large audience, and at this dissection there were present a multitude of knowledgeable medical scholars and I should reckon that none of those who were present will say that I did not make my point in much greater detail than I have been able to do in this book.

It was he, too, who first observed and drew the foetus of the dolphin and the killer whale, always taking great care to 'recover the unborn offspring of the dolphins who were brought to the Halles in Paris'.

If it should be decided some day to award a posthumous Nobel Prize to the researchers who have contributed the most, within the limits of human knowledge of their day, to the progress of science such as we understand it now, Pierre Belon would undoubtedly rank very high on the list. In his works he lists the names of all the dolphins and porpoises and explains their origin; he goes to great lengths to demonstrate '. . . that if the dolphin is not known by the French as such . . . nevertheless they know him well, even if he is not called by his proper name.' The French then called the dolphin *oye* or *bec d'oye* (goose or goose's beak) because of his long round beak.

Like all who know them well, Belon was seduced by dolphins. He writes:

Nature has not given the dolphin external weapons. If he dominates and commands others it is through his virtue and not through strength of arms, as all he possesses to injure others and to defend himself are his teeth only.

He then continues his description without missing one of the typical features by which cetaceans are connected to land mammals:

37

His skin is completely smooth and slippery. He has no scales and his tail contradicts the common rule for other fish ... the dolphin has an oblique tail, as do birds. The said tail gives him great force when swimming. ... The dolphin can shut his eyelids in the same way that a land animal lowers his eyelid to cover the ball of his eye. ... The nasal passages, however diligently one may look for them, are nowhere to be seen except in the baby dolphin up to the age of one or two months, because after that as the animal grows they disappear. ... They may also be seen in the unborn when pulled from the womb, and these also have tiny hard white bristles on each side of the top part of the jaw, and if some of these are cut to the roots and the roots probed with a knife, one can see the roots inserted in certain nerves from which they stem. ... All other fish have ears which are openings on either side. But the dolphin has none ... and, as nature has denied him these, she has given him a flute, which runs directly above the head between the eyes, by which pipe he inhales and exhales air, shoots water, and makes sounds ...

In the same scrupulous detail and with the same exact emphasis on land mammal features, Belon also describes porpoises and killer whales 'whom the Latins called Orca or Orcinum'. Then, in the second volume of his *Natural History*, the author describes 'the interior parts of the dolphin and various other creatures of its kind'. And here again, by the justness of his observations, he shows that he had certainly guessed the secret of the evolution of cetaceans, even if he did not dare to draw the conclusions of his observations in an era where the world and the animals were known to have been created in seven days, just as they look today.

After a minute description of dolphin embryos which he observed at different stages of their evolution, he tells us, as an interlude, an amusing adventure:

This happened to a 'Mestre d'Hostel' of the Royal House who found such a big porpoise in the stomach of its mother that he could look at it only with admiration, therefore he thought it most fit to show it to King François, who was such a great admirer of works of nature that he expressly wanted always to be shown something new. But after he had seen such a big fish, that had been found in the stomach of a porpoise, he ordered that those be summoned from whom he expected to hear a sound judgement, but they were of the opinion that the porpoise had swallowed it and further explained that all fish eat each other, not knowing that porpoises carry their little ones so big, and deliver them alive.

After Belon delphinology died for two centuries. His successors again were mere plagiarists or compilers. There are few new observations in all the works of Gesner, Aldrovande, Johnston, Worinius, Charleton, Sibbald or Willoughby. Only in 1735 did Carolus Linnaeus, the great Swedish naturalist, establish his classification of the animal kingdom which, largely unchanged, is still authoritative. He defined the mammals as a class, including in it the cetaceans (with which, however, he also placed the sirenians), and gives the common dolphin his scientific Graeco-Latin name: *Delphinus delphis*. After him Buffon, Bonaterre, the Cuvier brothers, Geoffroy Saint-Hilaire and Lacépède published the first modern detailed description of cetaceans, but it did not add greatly to what Belon had said already, and until the late nineteenth century the *Grande Encyclopédie* continued to profess that 'the ancestors of the cetaceans were always sea-creatures, unlike the pinnipeds' (the seals, walruses and sea-lions).

With the theories of Lamarck, Darwin and Wallace evolutionism finally laid the foundations which enable modern zoologists to put forth their theory of a round-trip voyage, spread over millions of centuries, from the sea to the land, and the land back to the sea.

All that lives comes from the sea.

In the beginning there was the ocean, warm water, heavy with dissolved salts, heavy with countless elements where the incandescent lavas of the pre-Cambrian era, the most ancient of the earth's ages, were gushing forth in huge whirlpools of scum and mist, to solidify here and there in muddy crusts. In this world of troubled waters, of smoking mires and floating ashes, carbon compounds mixed with each other a thousand times, a hundred thousand times, a hundred thousand millions of times. One day some organic elements merged and formed a new substance, certain amino-acids encountered a catalyst, and suddenly something appeared which was living matter and which we now would call protozoa or unicellular elements, or bacteria. A microscopic tube, a tiny spiral, a parenthesis, which could reproduce by dividing itself, that is to say, to die without ceasing to live and without leaving a corpse, but, on the contrary, bringing forth out of nothing a new and identical being. These first living things were in fact mixtures of biological matter contained in a semi-permeable membrane through which nourishing elements from outside could filter into the body. Their life was nothing but assimilation, growth and division. This is the stage at which the virus has remained.

Throughout the long pre-Cambrian period these unicellular elements evolved, specialized, utilized the sun's energy through substances such as chlorophyll in order to make proteins and carbohydrates (sugars and starches) out of inert matter, and finally became algae, the origin of all vegetation.

In the Cambrian period, five hundred million years ago, the first true animals appeared. Already they paid the price of perfection: the death of the individual. They were crabs, they grew rapidly, to a foot and a half in diameter. The seas were still warm, the earth was all volcanoes covered with fumaroles. Four hundred million years ago, in the Ordovician period, oceans still covered most of Europe. The earth's crust was in continual movement, life crept only under water. Worms appeared, some with a flexible longitudinal rod which was to become the backbone. The worms with a spine were to become fish. Fish are complex animals that need water in which they can live and hatch their eggs.

The fish of the Silurian period, three hundred and sixty million years ago, began to develop coats of mail. Corals grew and spread. Some algae somehow survived when receding waters left them high and dry. They were the first to colonize the land. In the Devonian period some animals, finding themselves left on dry land at intervals, adapted themselves to life on land and became myriapods and spiders. Out of the innumerable fish which were left stranded when the tides went out, a few, those best equipped to live in air, managed to survive. They were the ones whose gills were in the form of sacs and who could obtain their oxygen from the air, whose skin could withstand the heat of the sun and whose fins were strongly veined and could serve as legs to go and search the ground for new kinds of food. In the Nile valley today one can still find some of these amphibious fish which climb trees to get at their food.

Others, to which some fortunate mutations had given real paws, became amphibians, animals which could live far from the water, but which still would not reproduce except in the water. This is still the case today with frogs, salamanders, etc.

During the Carboniferous period wings grew on primitive insects. Amphibians proliferated and certain of them took a decisive step forward: they laid their eggs on the ground. That is to say, unable to renounce the sea altogether, they built for their young a small individual reserve of salt water where they could spend, as they did of old, the very first part of their life: they had become reptiles. As the semen of the male was no longer carried to the ovary through the water, they also invented sexual intercourse. Many of the reptiles became extinct; others turned into lizards. Insects reached their full development and beetles, flies and termites multiplied. Lizards of all kinds and sizes spread over the planet. A specialized branch of reptiles became birds. These now made for their young a personal, protective and nourishing ocean contained within a solid shell. They evolved in their turn, becoming enormous.

For reptiles also, it would soon be the age of gigantism. In just a few dozens of millions of years the diplodocus would reach thirty-five tons, grow to eighty feet long. By the Cretaceous era large dragon-like dinosaurs fought and devoured each other on land and under the sea, as the birds of today began to roam the skies.

In the Eocene period the great dinosaurs became extinct on land and in the waters. Some reptiles acquired new shapes. In the Jurassic period, their bodies begin to resemble closely those of small hippopotami or big fur-covered rats.

Two transformations were yet to come: instead of placing the embryo within an eggshell, these animals now carried it in their belly, in a special container called the placenta, and there the baby stayed until birth in a drop of the protective ocean of its origin. Instead of the egg yolk on which infant reptiles feed within the egg before hatching, milk, the very concentrate of life, was fed to the young after their birth. Mammals had arrived.

They arrived with a new, an enormous, advantage: during prolonged contact with their mother, while they daily sucked her milk, they observed her actions, imitated the behaviour of their elders, and, once weaned, they continued to learn from experience. This phenomenon, the ability to learn, made mammals the masters of this world.

Fig. 1. The creodonts are believed to have been the early ancestors of the cetaceans. The skeleton of this one (a hyaenadon) came to light in the Eocene strata of Wyoming. He stood one foot high. (Restoration by the British Museum.)

At this time, amongst the Jurassic reptiles which became mammals in the Eocene period without changing their exterior aspect, there were some little quadrupeds equipped with a long nose and slender canines, dwelling in trees most of the time. Because they had everything required to survive and because their line of descent prevailed, we call them the Eutherians, literally 'good little animals'. It is from them that the creodonts evolved, thick-set mammals, heavy in form, short legged, 100 per cent land-dwellers, semi-plantigrade, possessing claws, and with a large skull hiding a rudimentary brain. Because of their teeth they were first classed amongst the marsupials. Nowadays they are ranged with primitive carnivores. Most of them became extinct between the Eocene and the Miocene, for lack of intelligence, but not certain creodonts of 125 million years ago, not those whom zoologists call eucreodonts (good creodonts). Because they were more suited to cerebral development, the eucreodonts, through a succession of changes, came to be the great-grandfathers of all carnivores of today, the cats, the dogs, the bears and so forth. And finally, during the Miocene period, the primates began the career we know so well.

There, then, is the overall picture; animals, men included, are what they are because their species has become what it is. It is not the individuals which evolve, but the species. If all the individuals of a species are ill equipped, they all die and the species becomes extinct. If most are well equipped, they survive and the species is perpetuated. If some are better equipped, they and their descendants have a better chance of surviving, and the species evolves.

All these transformations, we know now, have occurred through gradual changes, by a series of modifications due to hereditary mutations resulting from some recombination of the genes. If the mutation proved beneficial in the particular circumstances of the time, in the daily battle for life, they gave the animal possessing them and its descendants an advantage over the others. Obviously for each random modification which proved useful and each animal that succeeded, there were, during the ages, millions or millions of millions who did not succeed, who disappeared leaving no trace.

But what about our dolphins in all this?

Even if all cetologists now agree on a terrestrial origin deduced from study of the dolphin's skeletal modifications and of its embryonic development, they remained divided for a long time as to the exact identity of the land-dwelling ancestor.

In the nineteenth century they came up with 'pro-mammalians', but without really knowing what they meant by that. In 1908, some suggested the aquatic reptiles; others, later, elected a kind of primitive insectivore, not unlike the potomogale. We are left today with no more than three serious theories: a carnivorous ancestor, an ungulate (hoofed) ancestor and the Slijper theory. Supporting the first theory are the similarity between the jaws and teeth of the Archaeoceti (an extinct line of fossil cetaceans of whom we shall speak again) and of creodonts, those little extinct carnivores; the similarity between the intestines; and also other resemblances, often strongly disputed. In support of the second theory one finds only apparent similarities, almost unanimously rejected today. As for the Dutch cetologist, Everhard Johannes Slijper, he reconciles both theories: the ancestor, he thinks, came long before the differentiation of carnivore and ungulates.

In any case, here is a version of cetacean history which most biologists and evolutionists would approve today. Some 125 million years ago, perhaps because of an inundation of their hunting ground or possibly by the competition on land, certain creodonts were compelled to go and look for their food in marshes, rivers or estuaries. There, after all, the fishes, crabs and molluscs were easier to catch than mice. In the water, furthermore, they were protected from large, flesh-eating predators. As a result of random mutation, some of these land-lubbers found themselves with nostrils placed higher on the head, or with shorter, smoother hair, or with smaller ears which acted less as a brake in the water. These features, accidental but useful under the circumstances, helped them to survive.

On land they had moved about like horses, greyhounds or squirrels, and so they swam in the same rapid, undulating fashion. Amongst them natural selection gave an advantage to those whose tails were broad at the tip, offering a greater pushing surface, and narrow at the base. This provided them with a double rudder: horizontal for diving, vertical for turning sharply. Also the blade of the 'paddle', thus placed far back, gave great leverage.

They passed their new paddle on to their children; and on it went for millions and millions of years. Those animals which were hampered by a long neck, forming an angle with the body, disappeared. Others who had a shortened neck, well in line with the body, found it easier to hunt and to escape. They survived. Some first developed webbed forepaws, then a sort of mitten of smooth flesh which they used as a rudder. The hind legs, which were needless brakes, disappeared (except for small vestigial bones lost in the flesh, the remains of the femur and sometimes a small tibia). So did those animals that retained them and were thus kept back in the battle of life. On the back of certain former creodonts, now all smooth and streamlined, a pleat formed in the skin; it had the shape of a stabilizing fin, and was made, like the caudal fin, of cutaneous tissues reinforced by layers of connective fibres. It turned out to be a useful accessory.

Fig. 2. An example of converging adaptation of body shape in three classes of animals submitted to similar conditions in the same marine environment: the shark, a fish; the ichthyosaurus, a reptile; the dolphin, a mammal.

At first these creatures entered the waters only to hunt, and returned on shore to eat their prey; the otter still does just that. Little by little those animals able to eat under water without returning to land won dominance. Their mouth had lost its former connection with the respiratory tract and they could eat and breathe at the same time. Then, because they were safer in the water, they spent more and more time in it, but they still returned to the shore for the night; and it was on land that they mated, gave birth and brought up young who had to be taught

45

to go in the water. (This is the reverse of the way frogs and other amphibians, after taking to the land, have continued to return to the water to lay their eggs.) Seals and sea-lions developed from animals who needed to retain feet for use on solid ground, and they have stayed pinnipeds (fin-footed) because that was the perfect answer to the necessities of their struggle for life.

Many small primitive mammals took to the water at the end of the Cretaceous era or during the early Eocene period, but not all of them evolved in the same way, as not all of them were faced with the same conditions. In the sea, for example, the biggest amongst them escaped more easily from the enormous sharks of the period. They were the ones who had an opportunity to perpetuate the species. But in rivers or marshes it was less important to be big. The platypus, the aquatic opossum, the water-rats, the otter, the beaver and so on survived in spite of their small size; however, in certain rivers, where crocodiles and alligators played the part of the sharks, the water mammals became very large, like the hippopotamus, the capybara, the tapir or the manatees.

Unlike the sea, rivers and marshes dry up occasionally; in such waters animals which were too thoroughly adapted for aquatic living did not survive, while those did survive who could, in case of drought, use their paws on land to go and look for water elsewhere.

But apart from this the main features of evolution are common to all aquatic mammals. There is first of all an automatic system for closing the nostrils when they come in contact with water. There is to some extent an adaptation of the metabolism during diving, including a sharp slowing down of the heart rate. There are defences against the cold which are vital to any warm-blooded animal immersed in a liquid environment which takes from him, twenty-five times faster than cold air does, a thousand times more calories. The means of defence can be a layer of insulating fat, as in the cetaceans (some whales are protected by over a foot of blubber), or a water-repellent fur, as in the pinnipeds. There is also, above all, a complete hydrodynamic restyling of the body.

However, for an animal to be able to take from the sea its

inexhaustible riches, to belong truly to the water world, it had to settle in it for good. Eating there and sleeping there were not enough. There remained one last tie to sever with the land; to conceive one's little ones under the water, to bear them there, to feed them there, and there to bring them up.

For the new-born to survive its entrance into the liquid world, a few more necessary adaptations were made. The young dolphin is born and built like an adult ready to defend himself, the result of an eight to eighteen months' gestation; he comes out tail first, to avoid drowning or smothering if the birth is difficult (in land animals it is the opposite, for the same reason). As soon as he is born, the mother pushes him to the surface for him to take his first gulp. Because conditions of survival are harder, the milk of the mother dolphin is much richer: it contains five times as many proteins (12 per cent) and much more fat (40–50 per cent) than human milk. The baby dolphin doubles its weight in two months, which is three times faster than a human baby. For more than one year the little one, who literally lives in its mother's shadow, will come and suckle at her breasts, that is to say, come and have a big squirt of milk forced into its mouth under the pressure of the breast's compressor muscles. (Of the four breasts of the female embryo only two develop, and are hidden in two slits which flank the opening of the vulva.) As there is usually only one offspring at a time (twins are very rare), that one must survive if the species is to survive, and the mother protects it with just as much 'love' and as much stubbornness as a human mother would. For the same reason, if the mother dies or must leave for a while, a 'godmother', who has also probably aided in the infant's delivery, will take care of the baby as if it were her own.

Only the cetaceans and sirenians have attained this supreme level of adaptation. Placid browsers, the sirenians find their food in the shallows, without searching too far or working too hard. Their size, their sedentary life, and their tough hide protect them from their enemies (except, of course, from man, who exterminates them everywhere he can as fast as he can), and that is surely why manatees and dugongs survived in spite of their slowness and awkwardness and, perhaps, in spite of their intellectual dullness. They both descend from a primitive proboscidian; like their cousin, the elephant, the males hide little ivory tusks under their lips, and it is the appearance of their females, with their two breasts planted like those of the human females, which has given birth, so the story goes, to the myths of mermaids.

But for the fish hunters and the plankton filterers, for those who were to become toothed whales and Mysticeti, survival in the high seas required more exceptional capacities.

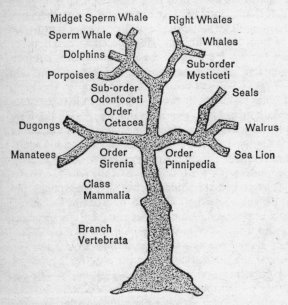

Fig. 3. The marine mammals today (a simplified classification).

Of the first stages of their evolution we have no direct clue, not a bone, not one petrified shape. The earliest known remains of primitive cetaceans, in other words of the Archaeoceti, are from the Eocene period. They belong to the Protocetidae, the first of the earliest primitives, and they are not much: a jaw and a few skulls which point to an animal closely resembling land mammals. Before that – nothing, hence our uncertainty regarding the ancestor's exact identity, an uncertainty which will last until we do find one or several of the still missing links.

Next stage: the Basilosauridae, which were advanced Archaeoceti. The largest of all was the zeuglodont, an Eocene Basilosaurus, the remains of which are found occasionally in some deep alluvial layers in the soil of the United States. The zeuglodont had a mammalian skull, very elongated (5 ft 6 in.), with a narrow brain; its nostrils were already on their way towards the back and its hearing apparatus was quite complex. It was sixty-six feet long, and looked like a huge snake except for its four

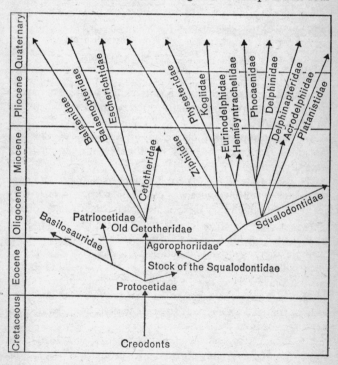

Fig. 4. The family tree of the cetaceans. (After Slijper.)

salamander-like fins. By and large, it was a Loch Ness monster out of a cartoon. Neither seal nor whale, it is not an intermediary stage between the common ancestors and the present-day whales. On the contrary, it is probable that its separate line of descendants has become extinct, like a thousand other Archaeoceti lineages of which we know nothing. The Dorudontidae, a few sizes smaller looked very much like it.

In the more recent layers of the Miocene and the Pliocene periods, which were formerly the bottom of the sea, palaeontologists have found in Europe, as in America, the mandibles, some teeth and some vertebrae of the Squalodontidae. These cetaceans already had telescoped skull bones. Their ways

Fig. 5. Restoration of a Basilosaurus (North America, 35 million years B.C.).

and habits were probably those of the killer whale. There were two groups: the Agorophidae in America, and, everywhere, the Squalodontidae.

Another group, much closer to us, was that of the Platanistidae, the direct ancestors, this time, of our various fresh-water dolphins.

The fresh-water dolphins are the quiet ones, those who have never looked for adventure way out in the wide wild seas. They get along, although they have evolved very slightly and none of them can stay under water for more than thirty seconds. In some ways, they are a bit like living fossils; *Inia geoffrensis*, for example, the sacred white dolphin of the Amazon and the Orinoco, still has bristles on its muzzle, just like a creodont; its fins, on which one still can see the five fingers of land animals showing under the skin, have remained rectangular and clumsy, and its humped head is still set at an angle with its body because the neck has not been compressed.

The Susu or Platanista (*Platanista gangetica*), who lives in the tributaries of the Brahmaputra, the Indus and the Ganges, still has a caecum in its intestinal system; it is black; and it is blind for lack of a crystalline lens. It gets its food by foraging with its beak in the river mud to dig out crustaceans and flat-fish. Its blowhole opens in a slit on the back of its head.

The dolphin of China, *Lipotes vexillifer,* is seven feet long, and dwells in the Yangtze-Kiang, and in Lake Tung-Ting. Its dorsal fin is not yet outlined; a mere fold of skin runs the length of the backbone and its muzzle curves upwards.

And in the Rio de la Plata one finds the smallest of all cetaceans: *Pontoporia blainvillei*; with its five-foot length and its 120 pounds, it is two thousand times less heavy than the biggest of the cetaceans, the blue whale.

Other dolphins, quite similar, inhabit the estuaries and rivers of Africa, Borneo and Asia.

More groups still: the Physeteroidae, either direct ancestors or extinct cousins of the sperm whales (*Physeter catodon*) and of the midget-sperm (*Kogia breviceps*); the innumerable groups of Delphinoidae, precursors of the innumerable varieties of dolphins; *Archeodelphis patrius*, distant relation of the porpoise; the seven fossil kinds of the Balaenopteridae and the four fossil kinds of Balaenidae.

Among our contemporaries the oldest cetaceans are the Mysticeti (whales and fin whales); that is to say, those with whalebone, who have no teeth. (Actually this applies to the adults, for the foetus of some Mysticeti have little teeth hidden under the gum, which disappear as the foetus nears birth.) Indeed they have a filter, in the form of three or four hundred plates of whalebone on each side of the upper jaw, to hold the plankton on which they feed exclusively – above all the krill, a shrimp which swarms in the waters of vast Antarctic areas. The whale swims into the swarm of krill with its mouth wide open, and sucks it in powerfully through its comb, which it licks every now and then to dislodge the catch, several kilos with each swipe of the tongue. The brain of Mysticeti is proportionately much smaller than that of the carnivorous whales.

The blue whale (*Balaenoptera musculus* or Sibbald's rorqual), weighing 130 tons, and 100 feet in length, is the heaviest and largest of all animals which have ever existed. We know very little about it, apart from what dissections and whalers' stories can tell us; its size and its home, the open sea, obviously prevent any direct observation and the kind of contact we have with dolphins. Therefore these extraordinary animals, which are on the verge of extinction like many of the whales, may become totally extinct before we have learnt to know them.

The Odontoceti are better equipped physically and intellectually to defend themselves against men. That is because they have had a much harder life. It was never enough for them simply to open their mouth in order to fill it. The Mysticeti are the ruminants of the sea, so to speak, and ruminants have only grass to vanquish. The Odontoceti are the flesh eaters; they would not be here if they had not been better armed, more astute, quicker and stronger than those they have to kill for a living. Their prey is fish (mainly for dolphins and porpoises); large squid for the sperm whales, and for the killer-whales, seals and even small cetaceans.

In the turbid water, sight was of little help to them. Their cornea was already protected from the salt by an oily substance secreted by a specialized lachrymal gland, but one sees no better in the water than in fog. Smell, obviously, was of no help; the nerves and the olfactory centres in the brain have disappeared or shrunk except in the embryo.

What is left then for them to use in a liquid environment? Cetaceans depend entirely on taste and hearing to find their mates, to escape their enemies, to locate their victims and to get all the information necessary for navigation. Cetaceans have a series of small, extremely sensitive gustatory papillae all along their lower jaw and, sometimes, also at the base of the tongue. As dogs pick up a trail by scent, dolphins taste it. Marine mammals urinate a great deal; sperm whales and Belugas, moreover, have a pre-anal gland whose secretions flow directly into the water, and this aromatic liquid (which gives its scent of musk to ambergris, the substance which sometimes forms in a big lump like a kidney stone in the intestines of a sperm whale) may also serve to mark their passage in the water for others of their kind.

But the recognizable chemical components of these liquids are quickly dissolved, so the major asset of all cetaceans is the sense of hearing.

The manner in which the ear of the mammals has become adapted to its liquid environment is quite stimulating to study. The instrument first appeared in the water. It was greatly modified so that it could be used in the air, and then modified once more for use in the water again. The mammals have devised all sorts of expedients to multiply and concentrate sound intensity: an external ear, which could sometimes be turned, a hypersensitive eardrum and a series of hammers and levers to amplify the vibrations before transmitting them to the nerve. On returning to the water, all this had to be undone, since sound waves move 4.4 times faster in water than in air and sounds travel much farther.

Another problem: sound transmitted in water reaches the skull from all sides. Consequently the sense of direction is confused, for men that is, but not for cetaceans, in whom the hearing system has been re-adapted to the physical properties of the new *milieu* in which sounds are produced and transmitted. The animals operate, in fact, two completely separate hearing devices; two ears which are insulated from the water and from each other by sinuses filled with insulating foam and by air-filled sacs. The latter are hard nasal sinuses which enclose the middle and inner ear. Sound, therefore, does not spread from the water all through the skull; on the contrary, it reaches each inner ear independently and directionally via the canal of the external and internal ears. If you observe a dolphin carefully you will notice on either side of its head, approximately four inches behind the eye, a tiny pin-hole; that is the orifice of the external ear, the opening of the liquid-filled duct which channels sounds into the middle ear. If you dissect a dolphin's skull, you will find there an acoustic nerve, very large in diameter, which leads from the middle ear to the hyperdeveloped acoustic areas of the brain. The dolphin's ear is much more massive and rigid than that of the other mammals. Such an adaptation was necessary for high-frequency transmissions, as was the system of suspension of the whole mechanism. But we shall revert to that.

To catch fish, dolphins had to swim faster. Cetaceans owe their speed to the high-output muscles which make up a third or even half of their weight. Their muscles are attached to a lightweight skeleton of which the spongy bones are 51 per cent fat, for it is not the skeleton which sustains them, but the water. Furthermore, dolphins take advantage of a perfect hydrodynamism and of a unique cutaneous device. We shall return to this also.

A giant abyssal squid, *Architeuthias princeps,* found in the stomach of a forty-seven-foot sperm whale, was thirty-five feet long, including the tentacles. To go after such monsters it is necessary for the whale to dive very deep, three thousand feet perhaps, to hold its breath for a long time, maybe half an hour, and then to surface without a decompression accident ('the bends') from the twentieth dive of the day, just as it did from the first one. All of this demands very specialized physiological adaptations, of which, too, we will speak again.

To kill such monsters powerful jaws were a must. To catch and hold slippery fish two sets of pointed teeth were an advantage. And to beat the dolphins, the best equipped of all, the most rapid, the most intelligent, the killer whale had to outclass them on their own ground.

All this certain mammals have little by little acquired in the course of time, from favourable modifications to advantageous accidents. Each organ played its part in the whole, and the whole, finally, turned out one day to be that marvel of adaptation to an environment which is an odontocete.

So that is the whole story – provisionally perhaps, for in cetology fashions change quickly and few theories have stood on their feet for very long.

Even the broad outline of this extraordinary sea–land–sea evolution is not above suspicion. In the highly respected *Zoology Treatise* of Grassé, Poisson and Tuzet one reads:

> In the cetaceans ... there is not one organ which has not been altered by their particular way of life ... the most extraordinary museum of adaptations which can be imagined, the fruits of an evolution which our poor theories are wholly incapable to explain, they [the cetaceans] show to what extent the organism of the mammals can bend to circumstances and be put in harmony with them.

And when, in seeking an explanation, the authors place

modern theories of evolution before the reality of the cetaceans, they arrive at the conclusion: 'To invoke a random
process is to challenge common sense and the calculation of
probabilities.'

A challenge to common sense and the calculation of probabilities? One rubs one's eyes when one reads this. Was this
treatise published in some southern state of the United States
where the law still forbids teaching Darwin's theories, where
one learns at school that the world was created in seven days, as
is clearly explained in the Bible? In Tennessee, perhaps, where
John Thomas Scopes, a junior professor of biology, was fined
100 dollars in 1925 for violating the 'anti-evolution' law? In
Arkansas, where another teacher, Mrs Susan Epperson, was put
on trial on the same grounds in 1966? No, not at all. This
Zoology Treatise was published in Paris in 1961.

I will leave it to Sir Gavin de Beer, a prominent specialist of
Darwinism and a former director of the British Museum (Natural History), to reply in defence of random selection to the
authors of the treatise: 'It is necessary to regard adaptations as
the results of random variations channelled by natural selection
into directions which are useful and thereby give the appearance of having been purposeful in origin.'

As for the so-called 'challenge to the calculation of probabilities', this is an argument to which Sir Roland Fisher had
already replied in 1930:

Improbability bears a different aspect when considered from time
before or time after the event. The probability that any man alive
today will have sons, grandsons, and successive descendants in the
male line uninterruptedly for one hundred generations is
infinitesimally small. Yet every man today is the living proof that
this contingency, so improbable as it may have seemed one hundred
generations ago, has, nevertheless, occurred.

Just as it occurred in the cetaceans' brains and bodies, the
improbable sequence of innumerable undesigned modifications,
their combination and their harmonious juxtaposition according to the laws of natural selection.

4

Two Eyes plus Two Ears Make Four Eyes

The dolphin's world is not a world of sights and smells – it is a world of sound. It is by sound that the dolphin finds his familiar haunts, by sound that he recognizes his loved one, his leader, his enemies and his prey.

The uproar in the 'silent' world is deafening at times. Malayan fishermen, before casting their nets, put their heads under water to listen to the sounds of the fish. Divers swimming among a shoal of drum-fish or croaker fish can clearly hear the noises that give these fish their names; they hear the rasping sound made by the large shrimps, the dry crackling of shoals of tiny young fish, and when they fill their bag with lobsters they can hear the enraged grinding of mandibles.

During the Second World War, the U.S. Navy maintained networks of submerged hydrophones at most strategic points along the American coast to detect approaching enemy submarines. The entrance to Chesapeake Bay, which leads to Washington, was surrounded by listening devices. One spring day in 1942 the loudspeakers in the shore look-out stations suddenly reverberated with the uproar 'of a hundred pneumatic drills demolishing a pavement'. The excitement which followed reached full alert proportions. Panic-stricken telephone calls were made to Washington. Then some old fishermen of the district arrived and reassured everyone. It was not an armada of submarines, it was just a million or so croaker fish (sometimes called black drummers) which had returned to the bay after spawning in the open sea. The Navy had no doubts left when they had compared their recordings with the croakings of a few captive fish in a near-by aquarium.

Certain sound-making fish rapidly contract and expand their muscles, causing vibrations to echo in their air-bladders. The croaker fish has specialized drumstick-like muscles with which it beats on its swimming bladder. Other fish use their fins and others still simply grind their teeth. Such vibrating sounds are picked up by other fish through their lateral line (sense organs lined up along the side of the body). What purpose does this noise serve? We do not know, really. In the case of young fish individual noises may help them to stay in groups, even in rough waters. Noises may also signal adults to gather for the spawning season.

But fish are only the noise-makers, the rowdies of the not-always-silent world. For that world also has its virtuosos. While swimming underwater with my dolphin friends, I have heard them snap their jaws in the excitement of play, make grinding sounds or multi-toned whistles or noises like a rasp or a mill-stone. I have heard them bark and make piercing little mouse-like squeals, mocking laughs, short groans that would mount in a crescendo and fearsome crackings like those of a falling oak.

When telling the story of Arion in 450 B.C., Herodotus took pains to explain in detail that it was by playing an orthian hymn, a shrill song addressed to the gods, that the endangered poet had attracted the attention of the dolphin who was to save him.

One hundred years later Aristotle observed dolphins at length, when he lived on the isle of Lesbos. He noted in his *History of Animals*: 'Although they do not have visible ears, dolphins are extremely good at hearing noises under the sea.' And also: 'They let out a shrill cry and wail when they are pulled out of the water, for this creature, which has lungs and a gullet, possesses a voice, but its tongue is not at all agile and it has no lips either, with which to produce articulated sounds.'

Pliny the Elder wrote: 'Dolphins respond to music, to the charm and harmony of instruments, particularly of the hy-draulic organ.' The hydraulic organ was an instrument similar to a modern organ, but water pressure was used to blow air into the pipes, causing such violently piercing sounds that the organist would play it only with his ears well plugged.

Since then many sailors have noticed how dolphins often flock around a vessel, apparently attracted by harsh grinding noises. 'It would seem', Lacépède pointed out, 'that it [the dolphin] shows a certain pleasure in listening to the regularly spaced sounds that are produced by pumps and other hydraulic machinery, however disagreeable to the delicate ear of a skilful musician. But unexpected violent noise will frighten him.'

Modern sailors would add that the piercing whistle which resounds throughout the vessel to call the crew to lunch rarely fails to attract the curiosity of the dolphins which may be in the area.

Frédéric Cuvier, the naturalist and brother of Baron Georges, also observed: 'Dolphins are not deprived of voice. Nearly all those who happened to be stranded on beaches and who thus could be observed, gave out plaintive cries that some compared to a feeble calf's and which others found similar to the broken-hearted wails of men in pain.'

Nineteenth-century whalers were reminded of the 'grinding of new leather' by the noises which reached them along their line, as if by a telephone, from the body of a harpooned sperm whale diving to escape them.

Now, since the Second World War, in which underwater acoustic systems and sonar played a vital role in submarine hunting, we have discovered something of which Herodotus and even Cuvier were unaware: the dolphin does utter cries; he does hear the cries of other dolphins; but he also hears the echo of his own cries.

Now that we understand this, and have been able to verify it by experiments, we also understand how in their evolution toothed whales have found substitutes for the sense of sight, since this proved to have a limited effectiveness under water.

The first inkling of this came to the mind of McBride, the director of Marineland Studios, the aquarium of Marineland, Florida, who, while trying to capture some dolphins, rediscovered something that all fishermen already knew: dolphins do not let themselves be taken, either by day or by night, in fine-meshed nets, even though they occasionally enter them of their own free will, if there are some appetizing fish to steal. If they are driven into a net and completely encircled, they will escape at surface-level, even at night or in rough water, one animal pulling the cork floats down long enough to allow the trapped dolphin to swim over the top of the net.

Wondering how on earth they could so well detect the least break in his wall of net, McBride wrote in 1947 that: 'This behavior brings to mind the transmitter-receiver system for the echo-location of sound, which enables bats to avoid obstacles in the dark.'

Man, when he wants to fly or navigate without visibility, uses instruments inspired by the bats: RADAR (Radio Direction and Ranging), which sends radio waves and collects the echoes, or SONAR (Sound Navigation and Ranging), which the British call ASDIC, which uses sound waves in a similar fashion. These actually are ultrasonic waves, that is, sound of such high frequencies that they are beyond human hearing. As radio waves do not propagate under water, ultrasonic waves are used under the sea.

Sonar nowadays is used by many oceanographers, by all submarines and by submarine chasers for detection and location.

The transmitter sends out a continuous series of sound waves either laterally or ahead. As the speed of the sound in the water is known and almost constant, one can determine, by measuring the delay between the transmitting of the signal and the return of its echo from an object (submarine, wreck or whale), what is the distance to the object. On modern submarines the information is immediately given by an electronic computer. Even the nature of the object can be correctly deduced from the particularities of the returned signal; a hillock of mud, for example, will send back diffused echo much fainter than a chunk of rock. But interpretation here is often risky. Moreover, variations of temperature, density or chemical composition of the sea-water can alter or garble the echoes.

A similar apparatus, but with the beam aimed vertically, is used by all ships to determine the water depth and the nature of the sea bed. They call it 'echo-sounder' or 'depth-finder', and it is the 'fish-finder' that fishermen use to locate schools of fish between two masses of water.

All these instruments are crude and relatively unreliable, and it is vital to perfect them, as much for oceanographers as for submarine chasers and in rescue operations.

As soon as the American Navy got wind of the dolphin's sonar, it sent its best agents in search of information. The Office of Naval Research financed the experiments; military electronics and hydro-acoustics laboratories and the Defensive Mines Center collaborated in them; private foundations, industrial laboratories and universities alerted their best physicists, electronics engineers, audiologists and biologists, along with scores of engineers and mathematicians, in an effort to uncover the secrets of the dolphins' apparatus and to try to copy it.

The United States' annual budget for this aspect of cetological research alone is just short of $1,000,000. The most active American researchers have been Dr Winthrop N. Kellogg of Florida State University, Dr William Scheville of Woods Hole, Margaret Tavolga, Dr John Dreher of Lockheed, California, and Dr Kenneth Norris of the Oceanic Foundation in Hawaii.

Dr René Guy Busnel carried out research at the Animal Acoustics Laboratory at Jouy-en-Josas, France, while his assistant, Dr Albin Dziedzic, worked in Denmark. Other investigators have been: in Holland, Professor Slijper of the University of Amsterdam, Dr Reysenbach de Haan and Dr Dudock van Heel; in Russia, Dr Sergei Kleinenberg and Dr Yablokov; and in England, Dr F. C. Fraser and Dr P. E. Purves of the British Museum.

Their work and that of many others from the West, Russia and Japan was presented, discussed and published at the 1959 meeting of the Royal Society in London; at the London symposium of Acoustic Biology in 1961; at the Convention on Cetacean Research in 1963 in Washington; at the Underwater Bio-Acoustics Symposium in New York in April 1965; at the Bimini Symposium in the same year; and at the Sonar Symposium of September 1966 in Italy.

Finally, it is only fair to mention the most important collaborators of all those distinguished researchers: the dolphins themselves. The name of Alice, for instance, deserves to go down to posterity. This female Atlantic dolphin was born in the blue waters of the Gulf Stream; she was first educated in the Marineland Studios of Florida, where she began her scientific career; she pursued her career in California, where she worked with the specialists of the Navy Missile Center at Point Mugu, and when last heard of was in Hawaii assisting in the experiments of Dr Norris at the Oceanic Institute there.

The most obvious conclusion of all these studies is that the dolphin apparatus is, from many points of view, more efficient and more highly sophisticated than the equipment now used in man-made machines, including the newest nuclear submarines.

In 1950 Winthrop Kellogg demonstrated experimentally what McBride had rightly guessed: a dolphin can navigate and hunt perfectly without seeing. When he barricaded their pool with sunken stakes, the cetaceans headed directly, at night and through muddy water, towards the only passage left open in the obstacle course. With exquisite precision they avoided transparent obstacles made of plexiglass, even when their eyes were covered with black rubber suction cups, and blindfolded, they had no difficulty finding and swallowing a fish thrown into the water of the tank. A series of machine-gun-like 'beep-beeps' replied to the 'plop' of the fish and only died away when the fish was weighed and evaluated. If the fish were deposited silently into the water the dolphins found it a little later, as soon as their routinely spaced signals had located it.

While resting, the dolphin transmits at intervals a series of exploratory 'beep-beeps', sometimes five per second, at other times one every twenty seconds. As soon as a sound, or an echo, puts it on guard, the dolphin sends a different series of rapid signals, hundreds of them every second, at a pace which increases as the object gets nearer. And, it has been shown, the animal's hearing is so acute that the sound of a spoonful of water dropped from a height of six feet, or even the dropping of a single pellet of buckshot, is enough to alert him and set off the fast location beams.

The sonar devised by our electronics experts works on a single and unique frequency and consequently receives a single and unique type of information, but the sonar made by the mother dolphin to the baby dolphin transmits simultaneously signals of a very wide range of frequencies; these range from the low frequencies that our underwater microphones can pick up and which our ear recognizes as cracks or grindings, up to frequencies ten times higher than those a man can hear, that is to say, from 100 cycles per second to about 150,000 cycles per second. It is because of this fantastic range in its transmitted sounds that the dolphin, when under water, receives a variety of information that remains totally unavailable to submarines. Very low frequency sounds are more suitable for long-distance

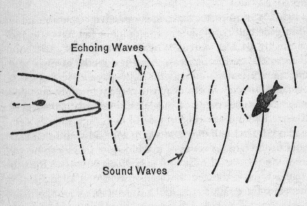

Fig. 6. The dolphin's sonar.

detection (half a mile or more for the dolphin, six to seven miles for the sperm whale), since they spread through the waters without being deflected. High frequency sounds, on the other hand, allow for an extremely detailed differentiation of near-by objects.

Kellogg proved that captive dolphins can distinguish at a distance between fish of slightly different sizes and that they are also able to choose, with their eyes bandaged, between fish of different species, say mullets or sprats, one of which they might prefer. He showed also that they can, without any hesitation, differentiate between a real fish and a water-filled plastic bag in the shape of a fish.

Dolphins thus have a most extraordinary instrument which indicates not only distances, but also the shape, texture, rigidity – all the mechanical characteristics of the object from which the signals rebound. From one single burst of sound they can obtain all the information that men can collect only through an arduous combination of sight, touch and taste.

The accuracy of the apparatus is astonishing: for the reward of a few grey mullets, the dolphin Alice learned to play a game with Dr Norris which consisted of choosing, with both eyes covered, between two steel balls and pushing the lever on which the largest ball was attached. Twenty consecutive times, without hesitation or mistake, Alice chose between one-and-a-half-inch and two-and-a-half-inch balls. Then she did the same with the two-inch and two-and-a-half-inch balls. Finally, where the experimenters were incapable of perceiving, with the naked eye, the difference between a two-and-a-quarter-inch ball and one of two and a half inches, and had to resort to slide-callipers to measure the diameters precisely, the dolphin distinguished between them nine times out of ten.

The degree of definition obtained by the apparatus is no less astonishing. McBride, while dolphin-hunting, established that the threshold of definition of the Atlantic dolphin's sonar is such that it will detect the echo of all nets from those made of the finest tulle to those of nine-inch mesh. If the mesh is larger, the animals often swim smack into the nets because their 'beep-beep' goes through it; unless, as William Scheville points out, a curtain of minute air bubbles escapes from the net (which happens if it has been freshly put into the water), in which case the curtain sends back the echoes.

The French biologists now at work at the Anton Bruun Oceanographic Institute at Stribb, Denmark, have shown that porpoises (*Phocaena phocaena*) do detect obstacles made of simple metallic thread so long as the thread is more than $\frac{2}{10}$ mm in diameter.

The mechanism and the operational techniques of dolphin

sonar is one of the subjects on which, at each symposium, specialists mutually exchange acid criticism, contradictory demonstrations and finally sarcasm.

Without going into the details of their disputes, we may say that the sonar signals of the dolphin are produced by a system of sacs and internal valves which compress, rapidly and repeatedly, air taken from the respiratory system. The signals are aimed through two little horn-shaped organs on each side of the nasal passage and, thanks to bony reflectors in the frontal region of the skull, can be concentrated in two straight beams, like the adjustable reflector of an electric torch. This gives the transmitters a precision of which the crude man-made sonars are wholly incapable. When a Beluga (little white whale) sends out a series of impulses one can clearly see the 'melon' (the hump of blubber on the forehead of the animal) change shape according to the particular sounds being produced.

Sometimes the swimming dolphin sweeps the horizon with a regular movement of his head (20 to 30 degrees) to explore the unknown or establish the boundaries of an obstacle, sometimes he will concentrate on a precise, strategic area, either prey or a source of danger. According to Dr Norris, dolphins receive the echoes of the different sounds they transmit in different parts of their head; the receivers seem to be in the inner ear and in various parts of the jaw; in fact, when Norris covered Alice's lower jaw with a sponge-rubber muzzle, she appeared to have the greatest difficulty in accomplishing normally easy tests, for she then tried to adjust to this unexpected difficulty by crying out her signals so loudly and at such low frequency that Norris could hear them from outside the water. Animal sonar is thus an instrument of stereophonic transmission and multiple-echo reception. Anatomists have shown that, from the receivers, the echo is immediately transmitted to the brain, at the same speed as in the water, through two little canals filled with oil-impregnated liquid. And this remarkable instrument, as Dr Sydney Galler of the Office of Naval Research emphasized with envy, 'is a marvel of microminiaturization as it only weighs a few pounds'. Men may envy it, but so far they have not been able to disrupt it or find a flaw in it: sonar signals, which to human ears appear identical to those of dolphins, and recordings of actual dolphin signals, have been transmitted to dolphins in tanks in order to deceive or confuse them; the dolphins, after a moment of attention, ignored them and continued to swim about unconcerned.

What utterly discourages the electronics experts is that on top of this infallible sonar the dolphin also has at its disposal two good, sharp eyes for use in clear waters, and can even see clearly in the air!

After many years of uninterrupted research, Winthrop Kellogg cannot hide his admiration for the complexity of the dolphin's sonar apparatus and for the way in which, like a computer, it makes a continuous synthesis of the information it receives.

During a conversation with another human being we hear a sound directed at us, for us and precisely adjusted to our hearing capacities. We normally never hear the echo of that sound. But the dolphin can only interpret echoes, and then echoes which he must pick up among a hundred others. Every signal he sends is returned by numerous obstacles – it strikes both the bottom and the surface, rebounds from one to the other several times, bouncing off other dolphins or the fish in the area on the way. Thus where each echo finally returns it is mixed with dozens of signals from the same dolphin, reflected directly or indirectly, and a thousand other noises of the sea, including the echoes made by all the other dolphins. To isolate a particular signal from this mass of sonar reverberations, and to deduce from it the distance, the direction, the speed, the size, shape and texture of the reverberating object, takes a computing system, that is to say, a brain, of fantastic complexity. Dolphins can isolate, interpret and analyse simultaneously several signals of varied frequencies; deduce from them geographical information and the respective positions of the other dolphins of the group, in order to work out appropriate hunting tactics; discuss plans with the other hunters and to select the choicest fish, all the while avoiding nets. To do all this, and dolphins do it as the most natural thing in the world, takes a brain which surpasses the most complicated electronic computers, and which in this regard surpasses the human brain. It even surpasses our capacity to conceive it.

The whalebone whales, which seem to have a delicate sense of hearing, do not have sonar equipment, at least men have never registered sounds which could be said with certainty to come from a mysticete. Amongst toothed whales the open-sea dwellers seem to use a narrower sound range than those living in coastal waters and their sonar seems less sophisticated. Yet coastal waters are often troubled and have rocky contours that complicate ranging operations; their dangerous play of currents and tides, and the shallow depths which send back a million and one echoes and counter-echoes, demand expert navigators.

All researchers today agree that the future of cetacean-sonar research does not lie in the tanks of institutions. To make a serious study of marine animals it is necessary to study them in their natural environment, in the sea. In captivity animals do not use their total normal vocabulary nor the full reach of their sonar; moreover, the echoes sent back by the walls of the tanks confuse the recordings.

There are several possible approaches to the scientific study of free cetaceans in the open sea.

The first approach is to study them from a boat. This is difficult, for first you must find them, and then get close to them. Your boat must not make any noise; you need high quality hydrophones and they must be placed in the water at some distance from the boat; you need a stable source of electricity, powerful amplifiers and a very sensitive recorder. All this equipment exists, but getting it to work at sea is tricky. Sperm whales, for example, will let you approach with confidence, which enabled William Scheville to make recordings of their routine signals, starting several miles away and continuing until he was in their immediate vicinity. He even recorded their conversations – each of their phrases ends in a 'spoken signature', a personal way of ending the message which identifies the speaker. But dolphins are often more suspicious: as soon as a boat stops near them they disappear.

The second approach is to study trained animals in the open sea, using the same techniques on dolphins, who willingly co-operate with the experimenters; this has been done very successfully in a series of tests made for the American Navy off the Bahamas, where the dolphins Dolly and Dinah worked in close collaboration with scientists based on the research vessel *Sea Hunter*.

The third possibility is a variation of the second: *Sea Hunter* is also the tender-vessel for a small underwater observation craft, the Perry Cubmarine, thanks to which researchers are able to follow the tame dolphin under the sea, all instruments running, as deep as six hundred feet if necessary, in order to record the sounds and the echoes as they are modified by the increasing water-depth.

The fourth method, obviously thought of by an armchair researcher, is possible only in exceptionally clear waters. At Bimini, where a skin diver can see two hundred feet in every direction, a fixed series of cameras and recorders has been functioning night and day, at a depth of sixty feet, to capture simultaneously the image and the sounds of passing sea animals.

Unfortunately, in seven months of watching, the submerged cameras of Bimini had not seen the smallest cetacean pass before their lenses, although the recorders often caught their far-off noises. A compromise solution remains: to place the groups of camera-recorders in the corner of a huge submerged cage or in a small bay whose mouth has been sealed off. Such arrangements would be closer to natural surroundings than a concrete tank.

Amidst all the research being carried out more and more actively for military or purely scientific purposes, the National Institute of Health of the United States has recently struck a humanitarian note: 400,000 blind people throughout the country are still reduced to using the most incredibly primitive system of echo-localization in order to get about: a white cane which the blind person taps on the ground with every step he takes. Might not the dolphins show the electronics experts how to construct a more refined personal sonar for the benefit of the blind?

5

Will Men Talk with Dolphins?

Among the many sounds in the dolphin's repertoire some are merely utilitarian, particularly those which sound like a creaking door with rusted hinges. We know that these are used for echo-location. They may also, however, carry subtle messages to other dolphins. Perhaps the same kind of message a man reads in the sonar of a pretty girl; that is, in her eyes.

But what about the other sounds? In 1962 Dr John Dreher, a Californian acoustics expert turned cetologist, was conducting research on the Pacific grey whale on board the research ship *Sea Quest*. Across a channel south of San Diego he submerged a complex experimental device consisting of a series of aluminium poles, cables, hydroplanes, and so on. Suddenly, five hundred yards away from the barrier, he noticed a group of five dolphins who were heading straight towards it. As soon as the underwater microphones were connected, they relayed to the loudspeakers the grinding of the dolphins' sonars. The signals were evenly spaced, evidently just routine emissions. At a distance of four hundred yards the dolphins stopped and appeared to gather together, all emissions ceasing. Then one dolphin broke away from the group and, as a scout might do, came along to inspect the obstacles by sonar, closely, methodically, from left to right. He returned to the waiting group and the microphones transmitted what seemed to be a general discussion. The reconnaissance of the 'scout' and the 'group discussions' were repeated three times. Then the majority, or perhaps the leader, apparently decided that the strange poles were harmless, for the group resumed its course and quietly passed through.

Puzzled by this story, Dr Jarvis Bastian, a psychologist at the University of California, recently decided to conduct a similar experiment in the laboratory. The best approach, he thought, would be to place two dolphins in a predicament where they would be forced to employ a system of vocal communication, that is, talk to each other, in order to extricate themselves. If they managed to find a way out, then the demonstration would be complete.

Using a male and a female dolphin, Buzz and Doris, he set about to make clear to them, step by step, exactly what he wanted from them.

First he showed each of them two underwater levers to push. The levers controlled two mechanisms for distributing mackerel; to obtain the reward they had to push the lever on the right when a continuous light came on, and the lever on the left when the light was flickering. Up to this point, it was child's play.

For the second stage he introduced a new rule. When the light, either continuous or intermittent, came on, Doris, on her side of the pool, was to wait until Buzz had pushed the correct lever on his side. If she was the first to push, no fish. Still no problems. After a few attempts, it was child's play again.

But for the third stage of the experiment Dr Bastian separated the two dolphins by a curtain so arranged that they could still hear each other quite well, but could no longer see either each other or the other's light.

What would happen when Bastian gave Doris a signal which was invisible to Buzz, and which she could not answer herself before Buzz had released his own lever? And how would Buzz know which was the correct one?

Bastian switched on the continuous light opposite Doris. Doris waited as instructed, but she was heard to give a sound signal. Buzz immediately pushed the right-hand lever, the correct one, then Doris too pushed her lever and she received her fresh fish.

Bastian repeated the experiment fifty times, and on the basis of Doris's information, Buzz reacted correctly forty-eight times.

Scientific literature today is filled with similar examples and so are the stories of fisherman, sailors and whalers. The evidence is so abundant that it is becoming impossible to deny that dolphins and other toothed cetaceans possess a complex language and also a complex social organization.

During a recent expedition in the Antarctic, a Norwegian whaling fleet received a radio call for help from a deep-sea fishing fleet. A band of several thousand killer whales had arrived in the fishing area and was so thoroughly decimating the fish that the fishermen no longer saw a scale. Killer whales (*Orcinus orca*) are very large – twenty feet and longer – and very voracious cousins of the dolphin.

The whalers sent out three boats, each equipped with a harpoon gun. One of them fired a single shot, and the harpoon with its explosive head wounded or killed a whale. Within half an hour all cetaceans had completely disappeared from the surface of the sea around the gunboats, but they remained just as active and voracious around the fishing-boats. Now the fishing-boats and gunboats were identical, both types being converted Second World War corvettes. They had the same silhouette above the water, the same hull, the same engine, and therefore made the same noise; the only difference was a small harpoon gun on the bow.

Obviously the wounded whale, or other whales who had witnessed the incident, had immediately spread the alert, described the danger and even specified the dangerous zones.

The fishermen, the whalers and later the cetologists of Oslo's Whaling Institute concluded from this that killer whales possess sufficient intelligence to establish immediately the relation of cause to effect between the harpoon gun and the wound suffered by one of them; that they have a sufficiently clear and discriminating eyesight, a sufficient power of observation and sufficient capacity to distinguish, among almost identical ships, those which were made dangerous by a small additional contraption on the bow from those which were harmless; that they possess the means of communicating not only precise information and descriptions, but also recommendations; that these are transmitted to all and received by all and that the spreading of their danger warnings is rapid, pervasive and 100 per cent efficient.

One could also, it would seem to me, conclude from this story that the cetaceans who first spread the alert showed a marked spirit of organization and altruism and that their solidarity, at least from this point of view, is on a level with that of the human tribe. But above all, and this is most exciting, the messages transmitted here do not emanate at all from the old stock of instinctive answers built up and shared from time immemorial. No, they deal with an unexpected peril coming from a modern object totally alien to their known environment. One may deduce also that the 'culture' or at least the stock of information used by certain cetaceans, far from stagnating or progressing with the slowness shown by other mammals (who, since the invention of firearms have not learnt to distrust them), builds up rapidly, perhaps daily, through contact with new situations. We can deduce from all this that certain Odontoceti display an almost human ability to adapt and improvise. This ability is, however, less developed in the Mysticeti (the 'whalebone whales'), which allow themselves to be exterminated (a million whales slaughtered in the Antarctic in the last fifty years and the Atlantic right whales almost wiped out).

Could we not then develop and guide the culture of a particular animal by placing it in close contact with man, and by exposing it to new situations which would teach it a new idea each time and finally bring it to the point of learning some sort of common language? And when this is done, would it not in its turn spread this knowledge among other members of its tribe?

The thought that it might one day be possible to communicate with a non-human creature, to question it and understand it, is the most fascinating I can imagine. It would open our minds to a new dimension. No exploration could bring us more. In philosophical and scientific terms, we would truly obtain access to another world and, at the same time, open a new world, ours, to the other animal.

Science fiction writers, who keep feeding us their stories of Martians, have understood this. But if I had to make a choice between Martians and dolphins, I should choose dolphins without hesitation. Yes, it is mainly because I love them, but it is also because the world whose door they can open to us is that ocean which I have tried so often to penetrate alone without help and at the cost of much effort. It is that ocean which covers seven tenths of our ill-named 'earth', it is that ocean of unanswered questions and unexploited riches in which humanity wades – while getting a sore neck from looking at the stars and ruining itself by building castles on the moon.

To prefer dolphins to Martians is a realistic and prudent choice. Science fiction always bestows exceptional intelligence upon Martians; comic strips depict them with huge heads, and it is always they who visit us aboard their flying super saucers. But such concepts are unsupported, and if a man one day lands on Mars perhaps he will find only lichens in place of intelligent life; in contrast to this, the work of McBride and Hebb as early as 1948 had placed the dolphins' intelligence at the top of the animal scale, well above chimpanzees and gorillas.

Mature dolphins have a larger brain than ours, one that has equally dense groups of cells and is equally complex. Such, at least, is the opinion of those who are 'pro-dolphin', for one must admit that my admiration for dolphins is not equally shared by all scientists.

In the fifteen years or so in which delphinology has been in fashion in the United States, the small world of zoologists, neurophysiologists, psychologists and linguists has split up into supporters and opponents of the high intelligence of Odontoceti. In publication and symposium, American, Dutch, French, British, Japanese and Scandinavian 'pros' and 'cons' keep clashing with each other with as much vituperation as the supporters and opponents of spontaneous generation or of the great antiquity of man used to quarrel yesterday.

As far as I am concerned, let it be understood once and for all that I am 'pro'. I am 'pro' without ever having dissected the smallest brain, or weighed a hypothalamus, or counted the neuronal cells of a frontal lobe under a microscope. As I am not a scientist, I may confess, without jeopardizing my career, that I have taken sides mainly for sentimental reasons.

72

The main bone of contention is the dolphin's brain – the organ itself, its volume, its weight, the density of its cells, its complexity and also the connections one can or cannot establish between the development of this or that portion of a mammal's brain and the development of intelligence. The exterior appearance of the organ is often compared to two boxing-gloves placed side by side. It is a brain development widthways and not flattened like ours in the direction of movement. This being agreed, all investigators who have ever opened a cetacean's cranium immediately sweep aside with contempt all statements of their predecessors before stating their own conclusions.

Around 1550 Rondelet, the learned French doctor and naturalist, author of *Libris de Piscibus Marinis*, had the curiosity to open the cranium of a dolphin, but before him Pierre Belon of Le Mans had published his *Histoire naturelle des estranges poissons marins*. Asserting that 'all the anatomy of the brain of the Dolphin corresponds in all its parts with that of Man' (Chapter VI, 2nd Book), he gives us a description of the organ which is perfectly correct and obviously based on his own dissections. Two hundred years later the great naturalists of the Enlightenment, Buffon, Geoffroy Saint-Hilaire and Cuvier, tackled the delicate point. Taking up where they left off their work, Lacépède wrote, quoting the *Leçons d'anatomie comparée* of Cuvier:

The ratio between the weight of the brain and that of the body is as one is to twenty-five in some dolphins, as it also is in several subjects of the human species ... and in some monkeys ... whereas it is sometimes in the beaver as one is to two hundred and ninety and in the elephant, as one is to five hundred.

Furthermore the eminent anatomists and physiologists M. Soemering and M. Ebel have made it known that, generally, the more the brain's diameter, as measured in its greatest width, surpasses the diameter of the spinal cord, as measured at its base, the more one may feel entitled to suppose a pre-eminence of the organ of reflection over that of the external senses, which amounts to attributing a high intelligence to the animal. Now then, in man the diameter of the brain is to that of the spinal cord as 182 is to 26; in the monkey called the bonnet macaque, as 182 is to 43; in the dog, as 182 is to 69; and in the dolphin as 182 is to 14.

We may say also that the dolphin's brain shows numerous convolutions almost as deep as man's ... and finally that it resembles the brain of man more closely than that of most quadrupeds.

Cuvier further writes, in his own words now:

But the dimensions and the shape of the brain of the dolphin not only make some of the suppositions that have been made about this cetacean's intelligence appear more probable, they would also seem to prove some of the other conjectures that have been made concerning the sensitivity of this animal.

Cuvier's data were not quite accurate, but he erred in good company, since physiologists, neurologists and zoologists of today treat with equal scorn not only the work of the twelve or fifteen researchers who have studied the same organ in the nineteenth and early twentieth centuries, but also that of their present-day colleagues (who return the feeling).

As an example, let us choose one champion from the camp of the 'pros' and another from the camp of the 'cons'.

A pioneer on the 'pro' side is Dr John C. Lilly, the American neuro-physiologist, a member of an impressive number of scientific societies, committees, councils and associations, inventor of various instruments and author of countless publications. He has become famous in the United States (and too much so for a scientist, insinuate certain colleagues who do not share the limelight), and journalists have labelled him quite against his will, 'the man who makes fish talk'. Dr Lilly's books include *Man and Dolphin*, in which in 1961 he summarized his first years of work, and *The Mind of the Dolphin* (1967), a truly remarkable and admirable book which gives a fascinating description of two unique beings: the dolphin and the author.

Dr Lilly is a very rare case indeed. He is not a specialist, he claims, but a 'generalist'. A humanist, he is also active in science ('I am a man first, then a scientist'); and what is most exceptional nowadays, he is a researcher who knows what he is looking for and why he is looking. When he began his work, Lilly, like so many others, first of all refuted the statements of his predecessors. He felt that previous studies were not based on material that had been taken from a living animal, and thus assessed tissues already altered by decomposition. On the basis of five freshly dissected organs, he affirms that the brain of *Tursiops* is a 'first-class brain', as complex as that of a man; that the temporal and occipital lobes are highly developed; and that the cortex,[1] differentiated in six equal strata, possesses more folds, fissures and convolutions and a greater number of cells. He adds that the density of the cells is 'more or less similar to that of man' and that the nuclei of the thalamus[2] are identical and of the same dimensions as those of humans. In other words, if all the nuclei of the thalamus, called 'nuclei of association', are present, it could indicate that the dolphin also possesses the same zones of association in his cerebral cortex as we do, in relation to these nuclei. The cerebellum[3] also is extremely large.

By and large, what Lilly suggests is this: comparable cortex—comparable intellectual superiority.

On the 'con' side, at the International Symposium on Ceto-logical Research in Washington, D.C., in 1963, Dr Lawrence Kruger, Professor of Anatomy at the Institute for Brain Research of the University of California, had this to say: 'The reviewer of this subject (the brain of the dolphin) is confronted with numerous contradictory statements, some verging on the border of scientific outrage.' In this introduction he also reprimands all his predecessors for having drawn their conclusions from badly preserved, and thus altered, organs. (A typical detail: in the first round of questions put to Kruger after his address a colleague on the 'pro' side arose to contest, on chemical grounds, Kruger's technique of brain preservation and, therefore, his conclusions.)

The most striking aspect of the brain of cetaceans, Kruger continues, is the large size of the cerebral hemispheres and the remarkable fissuration of the cortex. Up to this point there is

1. The cortex, or envelope of the brain, is more highly developed in man than in other animals and this development seems to be closely associated with intelligence and behavioural flexibility.

2. The thalamus, situated at the base of the brain is, in man, a sensitory relay affecting consciousness, mood, and the expression of emotion.

3. Situated under the cerebrum, the cerebellum is the nerve centre which controls equilibrium, muscular contractions, etc.

general agreement. But he immediately adds that the density of neurons (the nerve cells) in the cortex is low and cell differentiation poor, and that while the cortex has a large surface and many folds, it is also very thin, much thinner than the human cortex. And that it is, in short, much less differentiated into levels than that of the rabbit, or even those of all other mammals. In fact the number of layers of the cortex is at present considered the most reliable criterion of intelligence. Nevertheless, before definitively setting the intelligence of the dolphin below that of the rabbit, Professor Kruger proposes to consider it from another angle: perhaps the extent of the cortex and the complexity of its convolutions could make up for its scant diversity in levels? We know, he says, that the amount of the cortical surface used for sensory projections – that is, the utilitarian part of the brain which governs seeing, feeling and so on, and permits the animal to find its food and avoid its enemies – is proportionately much bigger in animals than in men (90 per cent in the rabbit, 50 per cent in the cat, 25 per cent in the monkey, 10 per cent in man). The remainder of the cortex consists of the 'zone of associations', where the memory resides, as well as the various higher forms of comprehension and intelligence.

He admits that from that point of view the dolphin seems the equal of the most advanced primates (apes) and proboscidians (elephants). But since three of the most highly specialized orders of mammals, the cetaceans, primates and proboscidians, all have vast zones of association in their cortex, it follows that what gives man his intellectual superiority is the high differentiation in levels, an exclusive characteristic of our brain. And, finally, Kruger downgrades the performances of dolphin stars in the oceanaria, putting them 'on all fours' with performing dogs; according to him they are 'excellent examples of the trainer's skill in reinforcing some variant in normal behavior and building it into an act'. And he concludes: 'On the basis of structural specialization of the cerebral cortex and behavioral comparisons, the position of the dolphin on the hierarchy of intelligent animals should be scrutinized with greater dispassion than is current.'

Let us take leave of the 'pro' and 'con' factors and return to figures: the brain of an eight-foot-long adult *Tursiops* weighs an average of 1,700 grams; that of a six-foot man, 1,500 grams; that of a five-foot chimpanzee, 340 grams – as against 31 grams for a cat, for example, or 0.4 grams for a mouse. Of course the weights alone are not significant; if they were, the elephant with his six kilos of brains, and the sperm whale with nine kilos would be the true intellectuals of the world. Lilly believes the sperm whale to be, in its own particular way and in its own sphere, a creature of extraordinary intelligence and one about which we are not sufficiently curious.

We have seen that Lacépède, like Carlson and Johnson more recently, proposed to compare the relative dimensions of certain sections of the spinal cord to the mass of the brain, a relation which determines how much the areas of 'elevated' function prevail over those of utilitarian function: a brain that is very well developed in comparison with the spinal cord would thus indicate a complex psychological development. But as the dolphin has no hind limbs, one cannot compare him from this angle with quadrupeds whose spinal cord controls more tissues.

The specialists are in disagreement as usual – some now propose as an intelligence indicator the ratio of body-weight to brain-weight and others the ratio of brain-weight to body-length, since both these measurements reflect the approximate size of the command area in relation to the mass of tissue commanded.

For the dolphin, let us rule out the second ratio. This will spare us from comparing man with his four limbs with the dolphin, which has only two. Furthermore, anatomical equipment and, consequently, nervous infrastructure, greatly differ between man and dolphin, even when body-length is equal. Thus the first ratio gives the following: man's brain, 2 per cent of total weight and dolphin's brain, 1.2 per cent. Compared with the chimpanzee with 0.7 per cent the dolphin does not come off badly! But Lilly, far from becoming involved in the ratio quarrel, employs a simpler working hypothesis: the absolute weight, from the moment it reaches what he calls 'a critical mass', becomes significant, at least in mammals comparable to man by their weight. In fact, if we think of our other cousins, those who are extinct, the prehominoids who invented tools and fire, we see that the cerebral equipment of the dolphin compares very well with that of the *Australopithecus* of South Africa and his chimpanzee-size brain (350 grams); with that of the Java *Pithecanthropus* (650 grams – the same as a baby *homo sapiens* five months old); with that of the Sinanthropus (900 grams – like a one-year-old human child); that of Neanderthal man (950 grams, or a fifteen-month child) and even with that of the Cro-Magnon man, who was very nearly our equal.

Now let us continue with Lilly's comparisons: according to the statistics of paediatric hospitals, a baby begins to imitate sounds at about five or six months, when his brain weighs 650 grams; the first articulated words come out at nine months (770 grams). At eighteen months the baby names objects and images which he recognizes (1,030 grams); at twenty-one months he combines words (1,060 grams); when two years old, he masters the basic elements of language; he forms complete phrases and ties them together correctly and logically.

It only remains for him, from that time on, to perfect himself in the finer points of syntax and to enrich his vocabulary, which he will do at the same time as his cells, his neurons and their countless new interconnections continue to multiply. Everything thus happens as if there existed in the higher mammals, whether marine or terrestrial, a critical weight of grey matter, more than a kilogram, below which a complex and organized language such as ours cannot be developed. So, reversing the proposition, Lilly replies in rebuttal of those of his colleagues who object to the anthropomorphism with which he approaches the dolphin: 'When an animal possesses a brain almost comparable to ours, it is no longer wholly an animal. Therefore I do not treat it entirely like an animal.'

If the dolphins prove by their behaviour that they possess a complex language and if, as the 'pros' assert, they possess the intellectual equipment necessary to master human-type language, then the idea of attempting to communicate with them is reasonable. In the last few years several United States institutes for scientific, industrial or military research have devoted much time and money to this effort. From a practical point of view the difficulties are enormous.

Technical difficulties; neither man nor dolphin is deaf or dumb in his own element, but in the other's element very much becomes so. It is therefore necessary to pierce the barrier of the water surface by putting in operation a whole array of underwater microphones and aerial loudspeakers, or, vice versa, aerial microphones and watertight loudspeakers.

Biological difficulties: the dolphin has no vocal cords; therefore he cannot correctly reproduce human sounds. Similarly men do not normally produce the sounds the dolphin emits from the system of internal sacs and pipes with which his skull is equipped. Moreover, and here is perhaps the gravest limitation facing the investigators, the range of frequencies employed by the dolphin to formulate his messages is phenomenally wide (from 2,000 to 170,000 cycles per second), while ours by comparison is very limited (16 to 15,000 cycles per second).[1]

We share only a minor portion of the dolphin's range, our 'very high frequencies' being the dolphin's lowest. Therefore we miss the ultra-sounds which he emits, presumably by means of contractions of the larynx; and to hear his messages in full we must rely on electronic instruments more sensitive than our ear. These instruments record graphically all dolphin sounds and transmit them to us in a 'translated' version. Or else we must call upon unscrambling recorders which by various technical manipulations change the frequencies to a much lower pitch.

1. A sound is a vibration which can be heard. What constitutes a sound, let us remember, is the periodic and cyclic compression and rarefaction of the medium in which it is produced and propagated. These compressions and rarefactions, called the sound wave, are transmitted with a speed which varies with the medium: 340 metres per second in the air; 1.425 metres in water; even faster in solids. In a vacuum sound is not transmitted. The length of a sound wave is inversely proportionate to its number of vibrations per second.

For the human ear, infra-sounds are those with a frequency less than sixteen cycles per second; ultra-sounds, those which vibrate at more than 15,000 cycles (or periods) per second.

Furthermore, a decision is needed: should man teach the dolphin English or learn 'Dolphinese'? Talk to him in English and listen to him in Dolphinese? Or should we jointly develop a new artificial language? An inter-species Esperanto? Let us look at the first method, that of Dr Lilly. To teach English to dolphins is to teach them to associate a human spoken message with its meaning; then to make them talk themselves.

In 1955 a group of eight neurophysiologists including Dr Lilly started a series of organized studies on Atlantic dolphins at the Marineland Aquarium in Florida. This first contact between scientists and dolphins was unfortunate. To begin with the researchers planned to identify and localize precisely the motor zones of the dolphins' brain and their different specialized centres: the centre of vision, the centre which regulates hot and cold, the acoustic and tactile centre, the emotive centre, etc. This cartographic work normally is the first stage of all research on the nervous system or on any aspect of the animal's behaviour. We have long possessed detailed plans of the brain of rats, cats or chimpanzees, for example. By stimulating electrically this or that part of the brain of the anaesthetized subject, we can register and measure precisely the electric potentials emitted by a particular region of the brain in response to each type of stimulus studied. In the first place, it is more convenient than evaluating a reaction such as salivation or shivering, and second, it gives the investigator a definite and reproducible method of stimulating the subject.

For this basic work normal operation techniques involve anaesthetizing the subject, but it turned out that cetaceans cannot undergo anaesthesia. As soon as narcosis began to overcome the first dolphin the astonished investigators saw his breathing become disorganized; slow down, then become irregular. Soon it stopped and the cardiac rhythm broke down. Death followed – a painful death by asphyxiation. After other dolphins were given nembutal and paraldehyde (two anaesthetics fully tolerated by the human body), in smaller and smaller doses, Lilly understood what was happening. The first mistake: the dolphins were kept dry for the experiment and the weight of the body, not being supported by water any more, lay heavily on the lungs and crushed them completely when the unconscious animal could no longer force air into them. Next, narcosis had relaxed the contraction of the sphincter of the naso-pharynx (a circular constricting muscle placed at the junction of the respiratory passages and the digestive tube which normally closes the larynx to water, whilst allowing the exit of stomach gases). This allowed air to escape from the lungs via the throat, and, as a result, the air inhaled by the blowhole escaped through the mouth instead of reaching the lungs.

This was understood only after the death of the fifth dolphin. The personnel of Marineland regretted this unintentional slaughter in the name of science, but the most positive result was perhaps that the eight researchers, for whom rats and monkeys till now had been mere numbers, no longer spoke of 'Subject No. 1' or 'Animal No. 2' but even went so far as to write about dolphins in such unscientific terms as 'charming creatures'. What is more, a neuro-anatomical study of the five brains, after they were preserved with formaldehyde, permitted Lilly to draw the conclusions which I have already quoted: conclusions made possible because for the first time dolphin brains had been removed under deep anaesthesia; thus were in perfect condition for analysis.

In 1957 Lilly returned to Marineland to try on dolphin brains a technique which had given him valuable results when working on monkey brains. The method used in animal psychology to teach an animal something or to measure his learning capacity is the same as that of trainers and tamers – it is merely the method of reward and punishment, a system as old as the world, and still the one which keeps modern civilized society moving. Still, the method is far from perfect. The proffered reward, a peanut, for example, may not be the most effective inducement. An animal might make a greater effort for a certain nut of which he is especially fond, but which is not found in our climate. Besides, it is difficult to determine the degree of temptation or stimulus (in scientific jargon) and therefore difficult to measure and to compare the efforts of the animal. There may even exist a whole range of rewards and desirable sensations beyond our conception. Also, the interest of a well-fed animal, or of one becoming bored by a game, slackens and he ceases to collaborate. Punishment loses its threat when the animal becomes inured to it or finds some secret means to mitigate it.

For greater efficiency, in order to control and measure stimuli, one can, as certain laboratories have been doing for years, short-circuit the reward or the punishment, suppress the object or the sensation which cause satisfaction or pain, and directly stimulate the particular centre of the brain which is the seat of well-being or discomfort. All brains contain a multitude of systems, some of whose functions are still not clear; the simplest are the systems of demand and the systems of refusal. It is these which Lilly had thought to stimulate directly in the cetacean brain. The technique is now routine: with a few hammer blows thin metal ducts are driven through the skull into precisely determined spots; electrodes are then inserted through the ducts into the chosen area of the brain. You then send an electric current of suitable intensity and duration into the brain and you have created an artificial sensation of hunger or of a full stomach, of sexual privation or satisfaction, etc. The natural nervous electric current is replaced by an external, artificial electric current, that is all. It sounds barbaric, but it is not really so, because a local anaesthetic desensitizes the subject's cranium. Men who have lent themselves to this kind of treatment report that it is painless. Better, they have experienced, as if in some science-fiction tragi-comedy, the hitherto unheard-of sensation of pure pleasure or of pure pain (experienced sometimes abstractly, sometimes in a precisely localized part of the body), or of total fear, or of true 'blind anger' or of deep irrational hostility. By similar techniques one can also stimulate certain centres of the brain with injections of chemical substances which trigger off typical physiological reactions.

Now then, it was necessary first to establish a detailed three-dimensional map of the dolphin brain, showing the seats of sensations which had failed to function under narcosis in the 1955 experiments. This time Lilly succeeded by simply using a local anaesthetic.

Equipped at least with an effective means of controlling his subjects, he undertook to persuade them to do what he asked of them, and what he asked was no longer to push a red lever like any trained rat, or to ride a bicycle like a circus monkey in a skirt, but to talk, or at least to repeat after him some of the sounds which constitute the English language.

Lilly knew that any rat or rhesus monkey can easily learn to switch on the electric contact which will stimulate his brain pleasantly; a monkey, for example, will push his lever with enthusiasm three times per second and sixteen hours a day, giving all signs of perfect happiness. He will even put on weight and be pleasant to deal with; conversely, the same monkey, if stimulated several times in the zone of the brain which produces pain, will stay awake as long as forty-eight hours at a stretch, his paw on the lever ready to press and cut the contact at the first sign of pain. Such an animal will become hostile, unhappy, lose his appetite, grow thin, and eventually die, if the experiment is continued too long.

But every time Lilly had tried in the past to change the mode of action to modify the rules of the game by asking the same monkey not to push a switch but to make a sound in order to trigger off the desirable sensation, the monkey had been unable to do so, even after hundreds of tries, repeated day after day over several months.

Apparently the production of a sound by a lower animal is indissolubly linked to an overall biological process. Cries of warning or complaint, menacing barks or clucks of satisfaction are not under the control of the animal, who cannot 'abstract' his cry, cannot use it separately from the total situation.

What would happen with a dolphin? Lilly asked himself, while installing a young *Tursiops* in a water-filled container, thickly lined with foam rubber in such a way as to form a mould round its body. Time after time Lilly planted his electrode in all corners of the enormous brain of the dolphin (known as No. 6). He located the motor zones, those which made the dolphin's eye move upwards, downwards or sideways, those which contract the left pectoral fluke to contract or move such and such a muscle or which cause an erection, and he plotted them carefully on the chart.

To find the zone of pleasure, that is reward, or the centre of pain, that is punishment, took longer, much longer – because there are in the brain of the cetaceans, as in our own, very large 'silent zones'; that is, zones which do not seem to respond to any electric stimulus and whose function is thus not understood. Then one morning, after many discouraging days, No. 6 replied to a shock with somersaults accompanied by a series of whistles, grating noises, barks and wet kisses.

At last! Lilly took courage. But was this really, as it seemed, a reaction of satisfaction? To double-check, he feverishly improvised a set of levers which could, by means of an interrupter, switch on the current that activated the electrode planted deep in the brain of the dolphin. The dolphin was watching him from the corner of his eye. Before the assembly of rods and wires was even completed he pushed with his snout just where he was supposed to. The current was on, the stimulus struck him and the pleased dolphin enjoyed an agreeable sensation. This was a zone of reward all right and, besides, he had guessed the rules of the game in advance, more quickly perhaps than an educated man would have done in the same situation, if but little versed in do-it-yourself electricity.

Other dolphins, when submitted to the same treatment, learnt equally fast on the first or second attempt to use their snouts to switch the current on or off, depending on whether the effect was pleasant or irritating. From then on Lilly could modify the rules of the game to arrive at his goal; to win the reward of the electric stimulus, the dolphin would now be requested to produce a noise, instead of push a lever. The trick which no monkey ever learned, all the dolphins learned at once – they whistled on demand. The first round was won. In a certain sense a rudimentary, unformulated dialogue was beginning. But here the surprises began. When Lilly replaced the system of rewards by that of punishments, the dolphins learned with the same speed to disconnect the unwelcome current, but if Lilly, cheating a little with the rules, kept up the contact anyway, the animal, instead of emitting all sorts of noises as he did in pleasurable situations, emitted only a systematic and simple whistling, always the same.

The two-part whistling, in rising frequencies first, then falling rapidly, was the dolphin call for help.

Sailors and whalers tell stories of wounded sperm whales suddenly joined by other whales who come out of nowhere to crowd about the victim and keep him on the surface. In aquaria and pools teams of captive dolphins have often been known to reply to a call for help, rushing to buoy up another who is ill or in a state of shock. Their aim is to keep his blowhole out of the water and protect him from asphyxiation (for the respiratory reflex of a cetacean is blocked under water, and an unconscious dolphin who sinks does not drown but dies of suffocation). The call for help is a real international SOS, a fact verified in 1957 at Marineland of California, by Dr David Brown, who observed a newly arrived porpoise, exhausted by its journey from the sea, being helped and supported by a group of striped Pacific dolphins and Atlantic *Tursiops*, in other words by animals of different species and even genera.

Other surprises: Lilly continually recorded all sounds produced by the dolphins in the air and under water. When he played back his tapes later at a reduced speed he couldn't believe his ears. During an experiment his wife had laughed; immediately after her laugh a dolphin had imitated in its own fashion, the explosive and repeated sounds typical of the human laugh. Another day he was listening to a tape to see if a dolphin whom he had 'asked' to emit a whistle of a certain intensity and frequency had done this well. All the sounds he had asked for were there, but in addition the dolphin had repeated on its own initiative the words which Lilly had spoken into the microphone, as aid to evaluating the tape later. For example, as an instruction to the secretary who was to edit the tapes, he had said: 'The T.R.R. is now ten per second.' (T.R.R. standing for Train Repetition Rate.) The animal had immediately repeated 'T.R.R.' in a very high pitch.

Further on, to identify a certain point in the experiment on the tape, he had said: 'Here three hundred and twenty-three feet,' and the animal had repeated: 'Three hundred and twenty-three feet' in its own way but just as clearly.

This he only heard when playing back the tapes at a quarter

or even a sixteenth of the recording speed, thus lowering the frequencies. But the thing which perhaps most encouraged Lilly to continue was a gesture from animal No. 8. 'Eight' had understood immediately that if he simply whistled as instructed for a given number of seconds, or in a given tone, the organizer of this bizarre game would press a button and he would experience a pleasant sensation as a reward. The game was in full swing, without a mistake, when the dolphin began in its turn to try its own experiments on Lilly. Each time the dolphin whistled, Lilly could see his blowhole briefly pulsating. At a certain point the dolphin added a new rule to the game, by raising the intensity of the pitch of each new whistle, so much that finally Lilly no longer heard anything. But he still observed the rhythmical contractions of the blowhole. The animal was now whistling at such high frequencies that the human ear could no longer hear them. When Lilly ceased to reward him, the dolphin emitted another 'supersonic' whistle, then a second, but the third one Lilly could hear again. The dolphin received his mackerel and in future always confined himself to audible frequencies which he had learned that Lilly could recognize because of his own experimenting. 'This,' writes Lilly, 'gave us all the greatest hope of one day seeing these animals try at least to meet us half way in our efforts at inter-species communication.'

Listening to the dolphins communicating among themselves day after day and analysing their dialogues on a standard acoustic spectrograph (an apparatus which translates sounds graphically, somewhat like an electrocardiograph), Lilly had discovered a whole new world of sounds.

Under water, a dolphin can produce three specifically different sounds ranging at least from about 2,000 to 80,000 cycles per second, each of them independently controlled and modulated; in the air he produces two other sounds between 300 and 30,000 cycles per second; and two more distinctive sounds in both air and water, alternated at an interval of a few milliseconds. Under water he will emit whistles, a tenth of a second to several seconds long, produced either independently or at the same time as cries, squawks and snarls.

Analysis of the sonogram of a conversation shows click exchanges and whistle exchanges. The whistles follow each other and reply to each other, about one every second; exchanges of clicks are more complex.

When one dolphin whistles the other one listens silently, except in duets which they indulge in occasionally, and then the first imitates and repeats the second's whistles. Sometimes, at the same time as the whistled conversation, they hold a parallel dialogue composed of clicks; the first one then will reply to the clicks, being careful not to click while his colleague is clicking, but may well whistle while the other clicks.

Thus dolphins are one up on us, for they can carry on two separate conversations at the same time, and on top of this they can keep using their sonar, just as men look at other objects when talking to each other.

To achieve a fruitful contact with dolphins, Lilly now understood that he must live with them in the water, talk to them at length every day, caress them, feed them by hand, share their games, in short, give them the same treatment received by a human child, for whom all the happenings of life, all needs and all satisfactions are associated with the words of the mother.

He decided to give the dolphins the same opportunity which his own children had had. First of all he would give them a home: a pool with running sea-water kept at a temperature appreciated equally by *Tursiops truncatus* and by *Homo sapiens* (25° to 28° Centigrade). He found the ideal spot on St Thomas in the Virgin Islands. He installed a laboratory there and had a series of pools blasted from the rocks. He then put on paper a long-term research schedule and, to carry it out, founded the Communications Research Institute. Financial support was immediately provided by the American Navy (especially the Office of Naval Research, Division of Biological Sciences) and by the National Science Foundation.

The first guests in the pool were two adult females, Lizzie and Baby. Baby was the talkative kind: when Lilly, just for the fun of it, whistled once, twice or three times, Baby replied by whistling once, twice, three times; Lilly would whistle again and the game continued.

Lizzie, however, had been hurt during the long journey by air and road, and refused to eat. Baby, on the other hand, greedily swallowed all the fresh fish which Lilly and his wife held out to her.

Lizzie's health declined rapidly in spite of vitamins and antibiotics. All day long she seemed to doze and Baby had to shake her from time to time to comfort her and persuade her to move a little. On the tapes of their vocal exchanges Lilly could distinguish both the piteous complaints of the ailing Lizzie and Baby's replies seeming to urge Lizzie to pull herself together.

One evening he decided to isolate Lizzie in a separate smaller pool, where he thought he could treat her more easily. The next morning she was dead.

Lilly understood too late that she died, or died sooner than might have been the case, of loneliness – of no longer receiving help from Baby, who had kept forcing her to fight her frustration. (The post-mortem revealed an infection of the respiratory tract.)

It is not a coincidence that the 'pros' are recruited among investigators who have lived in close contact with dolphins, and the 'cons' among laboratory theorists whose knowledge of cetaceans is limited to the nerve tissues which they cut in thin slices to examine under their microscope. All the figures and all the graphs in the world will never teach the 'cons' as much about dolphins as the death of Lizzie taught Lilly.

The Communications Research Institute installed a second laboratory at Coconut Grove near Miami. Lizzie and Baby were succeeded by Elvar. A younger animal, he proved more malleable and more curious about the ways of this world. From morning to dusk there were people with him in the water, feeding him and stroking him and he enjoyed it tremendously. This constant contact made him quite familiar with his upright, two-legged land cousins. At the end of one month Elvar was fully at ease, and was even taking the initiative in all games. His vocalizations, thanks to encouragements and rewards, were beginning to sound a little more like those of a human being – that is, of a human being speaking through his nose in jerky, chopped-up phrases – and a little less like those of a cetacean. For closer contact and to erase the air-water obstacle between them, Lilly had installed loudspeakers in the pool so that everything the men said in the laboratory could be broadcast into the water. Hydrophones in the water transmitted every noise made by Elvar to the laboratory.

What came most frequently through the hydrophones in the first days was a request for attention, a cry which we now know to be typical of a dolphin longing for company, the 'I feel lonely tonight' blues of these sociable animals.

One day Elvar was having great fun annoying a girl assistant of Lilly's by lashing her with his tail. 'Stop it, Elvar,' she kept repeating, while attempting to shelter her instruments from the shower he was causing. Later, when she listened to that day's tape recordings, she was dumbfounded to hear Elvar repeat several times in a mocking voice: 'Stop it, Elvar.' Listening more closely, she then detected a very clear 'Bye-bye' and 'More, Elvar,' and several other phrases of this kind.

Since he wished to talk they let him talk his head off. To the syllables: 'Oh-coy-may-lee-aim-woe-itch-why' and many others which make up the basic phonetic material of the English language, Elvar faithfully responded with a reasonably identical facsimile.

Of course the 'con' colleagues of Dr Lilly do not share his certainty when he states that he very distinctly hears imitated words and phrases so nearly approaching human rhythm, so well enunciated and of such quality that they are amazing. He is, however, the very first to admit that his ears give him a purely subjective interpretation of these sounds which he 'hears'. His detractors, whom he has had listen to the famous tapes, assert that they cannot hear the slightest recognizable syllable, adding somewhat perfidiously that, of course, if one does want at any cost to hear voices, one always ends by hearing them. Lilly replies that he has grown accustomed for years to the particular accent of the dolphins, and can understand them when others hear nothing, just as a mother understands the personal vocabulary and accent of her child, although its budding language is as yet incomprehensible to other adults.

I believe I, too, can say something here to refute the 'cons'. Often, during deep dives at sea or in a pressure chamber, I have

89

breathed a special anti-narcosis mixture of helium and oxygen. In a helium atmosphere, the vibrations of the vocal chords, although themselves unaltered, reverberate in a different way in the larynx and are propagated differently. At atmospheric pressure I had a Donald Duck voice, nasal, metallic, ridiculous. At two hundred feet my voice was completely incomprehensible, and more so at four hundred feet; except to other divers, or topside doctors and research physiologists, who had learned by force of habit and familiarity to reconstruct words and sometimes phrases from what sounded like meaningless squeaks to a casual visitor. Having been a bit of a dolphin myself, since I have spoken a non-human language which other humans have managed to understand by force of attention and habit, I believe Dr Lilly.

Lilly seems firmly decided to dedicate the rest of his life 'to making fish talk'. In 1960, summing up the results of his first years of research, he made a prediction which he has not withdrawn since: 'During the next decade or two, the human species will establish communication with another species, non-human, alien, possibly extraterrestrial, more probably marine, but definitely highly intelligent, perhaps even intellectual.'

Looking back on five years of continued research, he saw no reason, in 1967, to expect any rapid breakthrough. He wrote, however, in his new book *The Mind of the Dolphin*: 'I would suspect this estimate will be either too long or too short.' As he sees things now, the main problems are at the human end. Man's inability to communicate with other men, his prejudices and narrow-mindedness, hamper him in his efforts to communicate with other species.

A young assistant of Lilly, Margaret Howe, has devoted herself unstintingly for long periods of time to teaching dolphins English. In the all-new buildings of the Dolphin Point Laboratory on St Thomas she spent a period of eight days in 1965 actually living with a dolphin named Pamela in a half-flooded room where both ate, played, talked and slept together without a minute of interruption. Later she spent two and a half months in intimacy with a young dolphin named Peter. The progress of this remarkable, intelligent and uninhibited young scientist is recorded in her report and is required reading regardless of the depth of one's interest in delphinology.

For the future Lilly foresees a new type of relationship with dolphins. Sea farms, he feels, should be created where dolphins could come and encounter men if, when and for as long as it pleases them. Only then will a dialogue develop that is truly wanted by both sides, on an equal level, with mutual respect and with some probabilities of success.

In recent years Lilly has been associated in his work with Dr P. J. Morgan, whom he has placed at the head of the Neurological Section of the Institute, and by an anthropologist, Dr Gregory Bateson, who is in charge of the Communications Division. Their joint work has met with wider and wider interest. They have even been subsidized by the National Institute of Health, because, according to Dr Bateson, communication with a non-human being could open new roads of research to psychiatrists seeking to penetrate the barriers of the esoteric language used by schizophrenics. The psychiatrist today can only arrive at a diagnosis based on the attitudes of his patient, on his tics, his grimaces and the tone of his voice. All these forms of expression the dolphins had to replace when they took their plunge into water, and became relatively invisible. It is therefore possible, suggests Bateson, that they have succeeded in integrating into their language substitutes for the visible effects of our eloquent silences, our murderous glances and frowns, and he concludes: 'I hope the dolphin may teach us a new analysis of the sorts of information which we need, and all mammals need, if we are to retain our sanity.'

The Institute has also received grants from the Office of Naval Research, from the National Science Foundation, the Office of Scientific Research of the Air Force, and even from NASA after Lilly somehow succeeded in persuading its directors that if cosmonauts should ever have to converse with inhabitants of a far-off planet in an unknown language, the dialogue with the dolphins will have been a useful start.

Several groups of researchers have followed the road opened by Lilly, each with his own approach and his own critical spirit. 'We ought to be ashamed,' John Dreher was heard to exclaim, at the Washington Convention. 'There is little doubt that the dolphin can communicate with us on the response level and to a limited degree, and (to our shame) perhaps even in English. The only gracious thing that man, as the king of beasts, can do is to attempt to talk to dolphins in their own code.'

Dr Dreher and his co-workers Eberhardt and Evans are with a branch of the Lockheed Aerospace Corporation, the Lockheed California Company, which conducts research in acoustics and in anti-submarine detection instruments. The investigation work on the dolphins' sonar and communications technique is financed through generous research contracts with the United States Navy. The Navy evidently hopes to learn the secret of the cetaceans' sonar and apply any discovery towards improving its own instruments.

Dreher belongs to another school of thought; he tries to learn and speak the language of the dolphin or rather 'play' this language on an electronic instrument. He begins by defining what he is looking for. What he means by 'language' is: 'Any series of symbols that appear in a time-ordered syntactic sequence and obey predictable rules.' Whether the symbols are words, numbers, letters, signs or any sort of coded emissions is immaterial as long as they convey information which will modify the actions of the sender or the receiver and cause him to obey prearranged rules. With submerged microphones and high-fidelity tape recorders, Dreher has listened to the dolphin symbols he wants to decode and has gathered a remarkable series of systematic recordings of cetacean noises. He first built up his collection at sea, then in aquariums. *Sea Quest*, Lockheed's research vessel, carried his electronic equipment back and forth along the coast of California, recording for hours at a time all the sounds of the depths as soon as the fin of a porpoise or the small geyser of a grey whale appeared on the surface. Evans, at the same time, concentrated on observing cetaceans in an effort to relate their general behaviour to the various whistles recorded. Later Dreher installed his equipment at Marineland of the Pacific, the famous marine circus of California where clear sea-water pools and wide portholes permit more precise observation of dolphins and of the association between their noises and reactions.

Dreher has classified, statistically compared and analysed all of these numerous tapes. The result is a comprehensive table, listing thirty-two different whistles, which, he says, is not definitive. Each whistle is graphically represented by a profile showing its variations in tone, from low to high pitch, during the emission period. This is an approximate transcription, done by ear from a tape playing at reduced speed. The profiles may take the form of a 'U' ; an upside-down 'U'; a tipped-over 'S'; an 'M' with two, three, four or six downstrokes; or a 'W'. Sometimes they form a simple line or a series of dashes in one or two rows; other times they are composed of combinations of several simple signs variously combined, in complex variations and groupings.

The table shows that four of the thirty-two signs are all employed by the Atlantic dolphin, the Pacific dolphin, *Delphinus bairdi*, and the pilot whale. Seven whistles are common to the three species of dolphin. Atlantic dolphins and Pacific dolphins each use sixteen signs of which nine are common; and *D. bairdi* seems to have a unique personal range of eight of his own signals.

Obviously, as Dreher is the first to admit, such statistic material is limited. If all the animals listed in the table use only certain of the signals, it does not follow that they have their own dialect or that they lack those signals in their vocabulary. It may be quite simply that the situations in which they could employ them have not existed when the hydrophones were in operation. Dreher therefore hopes to enlarge his taped material to include a more representative sampling. He also intends to clarify his classification of whistles by inserting into them all the variations, all the possibly significant nuances which the dolphins use: length, rapidity of the slide from low to high pitch, grouping of signals, relative intensities of the different sections, lengths of pauses, etc.

Even though incomplete, the thirty-two signal table is still a useful working tool. Some of these sounds, at least those collected in the pool, have been recorded while a camera placed at an under-water porthole filmed the attitudes of the talking dolphins and the reactions of the answering dolphins. In theory this should permit an interpretation of the meaning of messages, and may, in a sense, tell us something useful also about messages to which the recipient fails to react.

Unfortunately the harvest of information from the movie cameras turned out to be small. Nothing new was learned, only a confirmation of the known meaning of conventional messages, typical of certain situations, like the SOS, the call for company ('I'm bored, come and see me'), the barks and words of love or the groans of pleasure. The only new signal was one of irritation, of discontent.

Dreher's team then reversed the experiment by re-broadcasting the identified signals from their tapes to the six dolphins (one male and five females) in the pool. A new reaction would then help to clarify their meaning, the sound responses would be recorded and the movements filmed. They carefully selected banal messages, six harmless ones which should appear convincing to the dolphins. (One day Dreher had inadvertently sown chaos and panic in the pool by emitting a signal that was apparently a red alert in dolphin language. So this time he abstained from sending forth the distress signal. Moreover, with no animal in danger near by, he would have been immediately seen through.)

Dreher expected a great deal from this experiment. Would the cetaceans remain dumb? Would they show an interpretable physical reaction? Or only a 'verbal' reaction? And if so, would it be a simple parrot-like repetition or a logical reply to the message? Were they going to panic? This happened one day with a solitary dolphin whom he had linked up by microphone with a group of dolphins whistling and echo-locating in another pool. Like a prisoner who hears voices and footsteps without seeing anyone in his cell, the poor cetacean had turned into a nervous wreck.

Unfortunately, as is so often the case in delphinology, the results of the experiment were to raise more problems than they would solve.

Dreher's signal No. 1 (recorded in the form of an apostrophe) the dolphins merely repeated, with no apparent reaction. They did this perhaps to get additional information, because the microphones also transmitted nine signals similar to the SOS, perhaps as an 'uneasiness signal' in the face of a mysterious happening, in this case a noise coming from nowhere.

In reply to the second signal (recorded as a circumflex accent) there was a concert of panoramic sonar exploration mixed with uneasiness signals and numerous groans of displeasure. Four suspicious animals turned their heads towards the loudspeaker.

At the third signal the male, suddenly in erection, charged towards the loudspeaker and stopped short. The others were busy looking everywhere.

The fourth message was one Dreher thought to be associated with a state of excitement and discontent. Reaction: a disorderly agitation and an uproar of different calls, while several dolphins, suddenly curious, undertook a minute examination of the drainage pipe at the bottom of the pool (the only possible hiding place for the 'invisible dolphin').

Signal No. 5 drew a few vocal reactions and general indifference except for a few glances towards the mike.

By contrast, Signal No. 6, an 'M' profile, with three downstrokes (No. 4 had only two), triggered off quite a tumult – inspections of the microphone, continual whistlings and echolocating and a profusion of signals with from one to five downstrokes, which were now altered, stretched, shrunk, widened, lengthened, in short, interpreted in a thousand ways.

The investigators became quite perplexed when they undertook to analyse the twenty kinds, out of the total of 694 responses recorded, and to relate them to the visible reactions. There was, as Dreher said, 'some ambiguity in the possible interpretations, the structure of this experiment not permitting [us] to say with certainty whether or not there is a link between the physical activity observed and the sound replies.'

All he could conclude was that the bell-like signals call for other bell-like signals and created an intense activity, and that another signal triggered off erotic activity.

As for the rest, it was thought best to repeat similar experiments with electronic equipment of higher quality that would analyse the signals more faithfully; and to use a computer capable of combining and interpreting the messages and of selecting and transmitting complex signals rapidly in the course of the experiment. In other words, Dreher is trying to find ways to converse freely through a 'talking machine' that would utter a pre-recorded vocabulary with the correct accent. By pushing the right button he could emit words and phrases which he will, he hopes, one day be able to decode and use, but never to pronounce himself.

Some of the fussy scientists who have blamed Lilly for interpreting subjectively the humanoid words which dolphins try to pronounce have also criticized Dreher for having transcribed from ear to paper the messages he heard and for having interpreted their sounds with a mere stroke of his pencil in terms of a 'U', or an 'M', or an apostrophe. The point is that science cannot very well digest personal interpretations. Science feeds more profitably on objectivity, on black and white. Science is right, doubtless, but on his own ground Lilly is not wrong. The study of language, of psychology, of human and human-like behaviour cannot be reduced to simple digits or graphs. A mathematician friend said to me one day: 'In love? Who, me? Are you joking? I'm a mathematician, remember?' Guess what has happened to him?

And then there is the story of the graduate psychologist who before his marriage had three theories on the education of children, and who now has three children and no more theories.

In any case, the energetic wings of the 'pro' and 'con' parties are now bringing into action arrays of electronic gear of ever-increasing bulk, complexity and cost. With a sensitive, characteristic tracing, electric oscillographs and spectographs translate on paper each of the peculiarities of cetacean sounds which the ear of the delphinologist might confuse or miss in the higher frequencies, and measure accurately such factors as length, frequency, intensity or modulation.

The cathode rays of the oscilloscope permit the study of very high frequencies by recording their variations on photographic film. The spectograph is an instrument which transforms sounds into an electric current. This current actuates a marking pen which leaves a track on a roll of paper, forming a meaningful pattern. For the layman, the profile of a long cry as 'seen' on the sonogram resembles the profile of the ocean floor as seen by a recording echo-sounder.

At the same time, on the other side of the Atlantic, Dr René Guy Busnel and Dr Albin Dziedzic were conducting Dreher-type experiments on pilot whales, common dolphins and Mediterranean porpoises.

But the French, working by night as well as by day, and on the high seas more often than in tanks, had assembled a much wider range of signals. Their acoustic-electronic equipment on board the *Calypso* (the French oceanographic ship put at their disposal by the CNRS) included a whole range of hydrophones, amplifiers, tape recorders and loud speakers, besides an oscillopscope and a spectrograph, which this time was producing results in black on white of the most impeccable scientific precision.

On his graphs, Busnel found five different pilot-whale messages, all distinct from those of Dreher and from those of Scheville and Watkins. From them he picked out a very important feature: that otherwise repetitive emissions are marked by sudden variations in frequency or intensity, which may be a clue to the meaning of the messages.

When listening to the common dolphin (*Delphinus delphis*, the dolphin of Greek and Roman legends), he analysed eighty signals recorded from the *Calypso* (or at least picked up by its instruments, which were not sensitive enough to pick up the dolphins' higher frequencies).

Five typical signals emerged: the first, lasting 1.1 seconds, is a brisk whistle interrupted by clicks, the graph of which shows a rapid fall in frequency from sixteen to eight kilocycles, followed by a slow rise. This signal is never emitted by an isolated dolphin, but always by individuals in a group. It may be a rallying cry.

Busnel heard signal No. 2, without the aid of electric apparatus, while posted at underwater portholes, watching the swift strokes of the dolphins swimming at ten knots in front of the ship. He noticed that the animals did not emit any air-bubbles when clicking.

No. 3 is a combination of whistles and echo-soundings similar to No. 3 in the pilot whale's dialect. It is the hunting cry of the group or individual. As Lilly had already observed, the dolphin thus uses his voice and his sonar simultaneously.

Signal No. 4, always emitted by a single dolphin, is the short 'U' signal (0.25 second) already observed by Dreher.

No. 5, very similar but even shorter (0.12 second) is the call for help, the same as that of *Tursiops* (the frequency in fact descends from fourteen to ten kilocycles and returns to fourteen). Busnel heard it repeated four or five times whenever he attempted to capture a dolphin with a harpoon or a lasso. It is not only an SOS, it is also the danger signal by which a wounded or threatened animal spreads the alarm. On five occasions when schools of dolphins were escorting the ship, Busnel beamed this signal into the water through his submerged loudspeakers. Each time the dolphins immediately modified their movements. They dived; stayed submerged thirty or forty seconds, much longer than normal; and surfaced, fleeing at top speed in a different direction, spreading out where before they were swimming in single file. Ten minutes later they resumed their initial formation and course but still kept a safe distance and still prolonged their dives. The same group of dolphins reacted in the same way several times to the same signal emitted at fifteen-second intervals. Sometimes the groups would split up and disperse. Three other signals, however, have defied all interpretation.

Later, when comparing the signals recorded at sea with those recorded in a tank in the Oceanographic Museum of Monaco, Busnel discovered that signals by captive dolphins cover a much shorter range of frequencies than the signals emitted on the high sea. Dreher likewise had noted that signals by *Delphinus bairdi* and *Tursiops gilli* were shorter in the pools.

However, the porpoises' emissions were all recorded in the pool because the *Calypso,* in all the years that Busnel worked on board, only once ran across them at sea. The echo-location emissions of the porpoise are very similar to the dolphin's. The whistled messages, on the other hand, are very different. Almost devoid of frequencies, they are made up of brief, repeated sonar sounds of a low tonality (approximately two kilocycles).

With his hydrophones, Dziedzic spied on a group of five porpoises, two males and three females, housed in a large shallow tank. From the 103 signals recorded over a six-month period, mainly by day, he isolated the sound which evaluates food; this is a utilitarian signal, not a message, which lasts less than a third of a second. It is composed of a click followed by a grating noise which the porpoise directs towards any food offered to him in order to find out what kind of fish it is and to estimate its freshness, just like a French housewife who sniffs at and feels Camembert at the market before buying it.

Next, clearly identified, was a domination signal. Three adult porpoises dominated the younger ones and would jostle them, if need be, with a blow of their snout. For example, if a young male while clicking and grunting in appreciation approached a female an adult male was ogling, the dominant male would give two or three rapid grunts on a rising fequency (the 'Hey you, stop that' of the farmer to a boy stealing apples). The young porpoise would immediately turn away.

When two female porpoises, the first of the group to be captured, found themselves all alone in an unknown pool, they kept sending out a signal of two hundred clicks per second for three days. Lilly had already noticed the same signal among the *Tursiops* in the same circumstances, one which recalls the frightened bleating of a lamb strayed from the herd or the tears of a child who lost his mother in a department store. The rest of the porpoises who later joined the two females did not cry. They found themselves straight away in company. One other observation: the love-cry of the porpoises is identical to that of other *Delphinidae*.

Busnel, though a pioneer in underwater oscillogram techniques, has no illusions about the value of a signal transcribed in black on white when it comes to analysis and classification. Of course an oscillogram gives a more accurate image of a sound than the 'I' or 'M' forms which Dreher classed by ear according to duration and variations in frequency, but it still is an incomplete picture. If two people pronounce the same word the machine will trace two absolutely identical graphs, whereas our ear will have distinguished immediately the voice of an old man and that of a young girl. We can only read an oscillogram, whereas the ear passes spoken words to the brain, which not only reconstructs the word and associates it with a meaning, but also informs us of a thousand details: the speaker was hoarse, he was shivering with cold, he was moved, etc.

'If we regard as valid', he wrotes, 'the hypothesis that the *Delphinidae* use complex combinations of sounds having intrinsic informational value and syntactic organization, then the methods of sonogram deciphering should take into account the smallest details, for they may be carriers of information.' Busnel does not fully believe that his method permits a precise enough analysis, much less an interpretation. 'What we need', he says, 'is a Rosetta stone for porpoises.'

But some recent electronic instruments are perhaps very near to bringing us the capabilities for precise analysis which we cannot obtain with an oscilloscope or the classic spectograph. Among these new devices is the acoustic spectrograph, which works from a tape. The recording head passes four hundred consecutive times over a very short section of the tape, each time reading and graphically translating successive 'slices' of sound, the frequency of each slice being seventeen cycles per second higher than the last one. All sounds in the range for which the machine is set are successively recorded in this fashion. The final product is an accurate map of the voice, similar in aspect to a bathymetric chart, in which each concentration and each deflection of the waves of vocal energy, due perhaps to the particular shape of the speaker's mouth, throat or even nasal cavities, leaves a record as unique and personal as fingerprints. Today this instrument is used by the police to catch malevolent telephone callers; by paediatricians to correct speech defects in children; and, still in the experimental stage, by cardiologists to detect incipient cardiac ailments that the classic electro-cardiogram cannot yet reveal. Tomorrow, perhaps, it will permit us to analyse the messages of cetaceans 'in their most minute structural details', as Busnel wished.

Another development: the Sperry Gyroscope Company of Great Neck, New York, offers researchers a new optic-acoustic-electronic machine, virtually a small artificial brain, which should enable us to recognize and classify the different messages of dolphins without any possibility of error and even to distinguish one dolphin from another. The machine, called SPEC-TRON (for Spectral Comparative Pattern Recognizer), is a tiny auto-programming apparatus invented by engineer Robert Hawkins to classify sound signals of complex and different frequencies. It consists of a bundle of very thin quartz fibres of various lengths, with a longitudinal beam of light along the base of the bundle, the opposite end of which vibrates in response to any sound. Each sound signal the vibration is different and, each time, each fibre, vibrating from its fixed base to its free extremity, more or less hides the luminous longitudinal beam, thus producing a dotted pattern of shadows and lights on a photographic plate placed at the end of the fibres.

Each exposed plate therefore retains the 'memory' not only of a sound but of a group of sounds, that is, a word. By means of a photo-electric cell, words (that is, several exposed plates) may be rapidly compared with each other. A complete bank of these miniature memorizing machines, comparable to a brain with its countless cells, could thus in theory accumulate and exactly catalogue all the elements of a complex language such as that of the cetaceans with a view to an ultimate translation into human language. George Rank and Leon Balandis, two engineers of the Information and Communications Division of Sperry, in this way have classified dolphin words recorded on tape by the Woods Hole Oceanographic Institute. They have shown that the voice of each animal can be identified without error. Even when the sounds seem similar to the human ear, the machine indicates that they are in fact of different frequencies.

In view of this, can dolphins' sounds now be recognized and compared with complete objectivity? According to the inventors, some of the *Tursiops* sound messages are clear and uniform when read on a Spectron. Others beginning from ten thousand cycles per second descend to five thousand cycles and rise again to ten thousand in one tenth of a second. Sometimes the same sound is repeated two, three or five times rapidly. These same sounds, played in a Spectron during a three-second exposure to light, have caused 70 fibres out of 350 to vibrate.

101

When played back, they produced a maximum current, whereas similar sounds made by other species of dolphins produce from 18 per cent to 95 per cent less current when played back into a memory pattern imprinted with the original signal. And the manufacturers, now looking for a market for their instrument, stress that the machine can help man to speak correct Dolphinese by permitting him to verify in advance the right approximation of words, or can be used to evaluate the attempts of the dolphins to speak human language. But just how would we use such a machine? In most laboratories animal psychologists use a kind of 'reward-giving slot machine': a rat pushes a red lever and a peanut falls into his food-dish, if he pushes the blue lever, no peanut. The problem grows infinitely more difficult when it is not a matter of distinguishing colours but of faithfully reproducing the whole complex range of sounds which make a word. The Spectron, the inventor suggests, could be the heart of a contrivance which, replying to a sound signal (the word attempted by the dolphin), would pass the image of the sound through the sieve of its memory and trigger off or not, depending on whether the sound was reproduced accurately, the opening of the automatic trapdoor from which a fresh mackerel would fall. Advantages of the machine: it works twenty-four hours a day without ever getting tired or bored or making an error, and it will never be suspected, as are certain researchers, who are only human, of taking wish for reality and of 'hearing' words simply because they very much want to hear them in order to verify a pet theory.

But dolphins, like men, are not precision machines and they could, being individualists, quite simply refuse to play with a machine.

After pointing out the limitations of the method he and Dreher used, Dr Busnel also had comments to make on the fundamental ground of language.

European researchers, especially the French and Dutch, are less passionately involved in controversy than the Americans, and their recent thinking on the subject has served somewhat to restore order. Dr Busnel heads the Animal Acoustics Laboratory of the National Centre for Zoo-Technical Research at

Jouy-en-Josas (Seine-et-Oise), France. Unlike many recent American delphinologists, whose fields used to be medicine, hydro-dynamics, psychology, industry or even defence, Busnel brings to the problem the experience of a zoologist who has always specialized in animal methods of communication. The paper he delivered at the Symposium on Cetacean Research at Washington, D.C., in 1963 has helped to enlarge the debate.

Tackling the problem at its very foundation, he began by underlining the differences between (1) 'phonoreactions', (2) the exchange of sound signals followed by reactions and (3) the exchange of complete sentences, or language.

On the most primitive level is phonoreaction, that is a reaction to a noise. It has been shown, for example, that a crocodile will roar if one plays a violin near it, or that dogs will bark themselves to death if one blows certain wind instruments full force at them. But these are only primitive reactions to an acoustic stimulus; a kick on the rump, another stimulus of a non-acoustic variety; would also make the dog howl.

Zoologists, have identified a wide variety of exchanges of sound signals in animals – insects, amphibians, fish, birds and, of course, mammals. For example, a hen uses about twenty different signals, a cow eight, a coyote ten, a gibbon fifteen, a pig twenty-three and a fox thirty-six.

If we sum up what we know of these exchanges, it appears that each signal is narrowly specialized, that at certain moments only one type of signal is used – the one that suits the present situation. There are no complex combinations of several signals, even when these possess a great number of different sounds. The invertebrates make simple and short sounds; if their sound is long, it is always the purely redundant repetition of an initial sound, which does not add anything to the meaning. As Busnel suggested in Washington, the dolphins' sounds could well enter into this category. If one examines the oscillograms of these sounds and wishes to apply a semantic value to their particularities, he added, one may arrive at an estimate of some thirty or forty possible variations. (Busnel changed his mind completely in 1967 in the light of the experiments of Bastian and the similar work of Batelle.)

Later, in regard to Lilly's talking dolphins, Busnel pointed out that many birds spontaneously imitate the cries of other animals and that in captivity parrots and crows easily learn to repeat complete sentences in all languages.

The small brain of birds obviously forbids an assumption that they might mentally link a meaning to a human word. But a mammal? In 1915 the Hayes published their famous book, *The Ape in Our House*, where they told of a unique experiment: they had welcomed into their home a baby chimpanzee named Ricky, and had brought him up with their children for two years exactly like one of their own. Ricky had learned to react to about sixty English words and pronounced four or five of them, rather poorly, however, in an explosive way. His vocabulary was limited to words like 'Dad', 'Mum', or 'up'. After two years Ricky had ceased to progress. But the sixty words which Ricky understood were not messages. They were sound signals, a noisy variety of gesture relating either to threats or temptations.

In the same way an elephant obeys the twenty words used by its mahout, but these words, which replace the horseman's twitch of the reins, and the whip-cracking of the lion-tamer, are only signals. This is conditioning by sound, a field in which exhibitors of sea-lions shine, since these animals react to thirty-five words. This is also the case, Busnel emphasizes, of the famous dolphin, Paddy, at St Petersburg, Florida, who distinguishes between the commands 'pull the flag' and 'ring the bell' and pulls the appropriate cord.

The capacity for recognizing and obeying words which tame animals acquire on contact with man has, therefore, nothing to do with true language; there is no intelligent association between the sound and its abstract meaning.

Only exchanges of sentences, when they involve one or several rules of combination which constitute their syntax, merit the name of language. This is equally true for non-acoustic language such as the signals of deaf-mutes or the gestures of certain monks who have taken a vow of silence. Their syntax, alone, gives them a complete meaning.

Haldane pointed out that even the human child, when he tells his mother 'I'm hungry' or 'I'm cold', is still only an animal who replaces two meaningful grunts with words. He only becomes a human being when he asks: 'Do you know what I did this morning?' By saying this he masters an abstraction and produces sounds not connected with his elementary needs or his present situation.

'And to this day,' affirms Busnel, 'in none of the species of animals studied, dolphins included, has any conscious link ever been proved between the sound produced and the object which the sound designates. Is vocal learning associated with the intelligence? This remains to be proved, and despite the remarkable development of the dolphin's brain, it is essential to admit that what we know about animal hearing does not tend to support this hypothesis.'

Today the Bastian experiments, in which dolphins told each other which light was on and which lever to push, have demonstrated that there can be a conscious link between sound and object and even between sound and an intricate new artificial situation. In a recent television interview, Dr Busnel indicated that he was now more and more convinced and closer and closer to the 'pro' party.

Now I would like to add the very straightforward opinion of another moderate European, a Dutchman, Dr F. W. Reysenbach de Haan. In the course of a remarkable study of the hearing of cetaceans, covering the mechanics of vibrations, their transmission by specialized appliances in the nervous relays, and their treatment by the brain (which he knows better than most), he states: 'In view of the degree of development of the cortex of the brain in the toothed whales and of other facts, the development of speech and language to a degree unknown to animals apart from man is highly probable.'

Let us follow his reasoning: on the most rudimentary level, fish perceive the variations in water pressure through a biological system known as the lateral line. An alarm signal, such as the splash of a stone in the pond, triggers off a mechanical reflex causing the fish to flee. In the case of cetaceans the warning information passes through the brain, where it is processed; and it is the brain which, after a short or prolonged period of reflection, decides which one of several responses to adopt.

Listening, therefore, is integrating information to situation and drawing judicious conclusions from it.

We know, de Haan says, that the Odontoceti possess the most perfect form of underwater hearing; we know that their brain, specially the cortex, is very near to that of man, which makes them exceptional in the animal kingdom; we know that they are able, using sounds, to ascertain their own exact position in space, or that of their fellows, or unknown creatures; to locate their food, and determine its quality; and that it is also by sound that they transmit all this information to other dolphins. Since many examples prove that the information they can transmit is very detailed, we have to admit that their methods of transmission are anything but primitive.

On the other hand, it is known that in mammals the processing of information takes place in one of the lower central zones of the brain, where control of the language function is also situated. The development of the brain and the cortex plays an important part. We have recently learned that the cortex is, in a certain way, a governing machine and control area that regulates the brain. If we treat the brain as an electronic computer, the cortex, then, intentionally delays the automatic response of the brain to internal or external stimuli, thus giving the necessary time for a choice to be made between the various possible responses.

It is a great advantage for an animal to be able to make a reasoned choice, and in the long history of the struggle for life this ability has compensated for loss of speed in reaction and has put the cetaceans at the top of the animal ladder in their liquid universe. De Haan states: 'The degree of development of the brain and the cortex of the Odontoceti makes the development of a language highly probable in their case. And,' he continues, 'speech conquers space and time through long-distance communication, imparting information on situations elsewhere and transmitting memory data of earlier events; and makes it possible to express speculations based on experience and to act accordingly in the future. Consciousness is a subjective experience of varying degree and is not linked to a given brain formation. It is, however, highly correlated with speech. Where there is speech and, therefore, language, there must also be consciousness.' In summary, de Haan concludes: '... it seems far from improbable that Odontoceti not only hear particularly well, but that they also hear consciously and understandingly. That is, that they really listen. I believe it is possible even to assume the existence of different semantic systems (languages) in these groups of animals, languages which may vary in their degree of development according to the species. The degree of consciousness and intelligence in each species would be directly correlated with the level of *speech* development ...'

What are we to believe in the end? As the old judge said to the jurors: 'Let us forget these torrents of eloquence and let us see, as men of good sense, what this is all about.' Well, it is about an animal possibly capable, certainly willing, to talk with men; about an animal perfectly able to imitate in its own manner the sounds of certain human words, and, unlike the parrot (which speaks without knowing what it says), possesses a brain well enough equipped to be able to establish precise relations between words and their meaning.

Beyond this fact, everything becomes complicated.

A couple of years ago, judging from the scanty data and the limited information available, one could draw simple conclusions. Since then observations, studies and experiments have multiplied. In the resulting chaos only two things stand out so far: the immeasurable degree of our ignorance and the complexity of the problem. After the first researches of Lilly and Dreher, for example, one could, on the basis of the sixteen recorded signals of *Tursiops*, ask this simple question: are these sixteen sounds out of the thirty-two in the complete catalogue, which are used and often repeated or associated by the Atlantic dolphin, analogical sounds? If yes, the dolphin can only communicate sixteen concepts; if not, could those symbols be syllables which dolphins combine *ad infinitum* as we do to form words and sentences?

There are two categories of language, Dr Bateson reminds us: analogical language and symbolic language. In an analogical language a particular sound, often onomatopoeic, standing by itself, represents a concept: 'Mama,' 'Go away or I'll bite you,' and 'Come here.' But in a symbolic language one must combine several sounds or syllables, which by themselves have no meaning according to the conventional rules of syntax, in order to express a word or symbol; and combine several words to make a message. A symbolic language, English or French, for example, lends itself much better to a wide variety of expressions.

To frighten an enemy the dog shows its fangs, the cat makes its hair stand on end to look bigger, man squares his shoulders or frowns; to be seductive, the peacock deploys its tail, the grouse dances, the woman flutters her eyelashes and smiles. But the facial expression of a dolphin is fixed; he does not resort to tricks or mimicry since they would be invisible in the water. Now the analogical spitting noise of a bristling cat is a clear threat understood by all, but the sentry's 'Halt or I fire!' is understood only by English-speaking people who know what a firearm is.

With the astonishing variety of its noise production, with a brain possibly as well equipped as ours, to analyse sounds, it may well be that the dolphin has succeeded, in the course of its evolution, in substituting sounds for the greater part of the range of postures and facial expressions which land mammals, man included, still use. We might then conclude that the type of language employed by dolphins will determine whether or not they will one day be able to communicate with us. Once we have determined this, we could then confidently start our search for the key to their syntax.

But today everything becomes more and more complicated. the sixteen signals are no longer sixteen; one may even ask oneself, along with certain critics, whether they ever existed at all, except in Dreher's ear and in his tables. Electronic devices now record other signals, but they are still quite imperfect. All Odontoceti, it is now established, do indeed exchange certain analogous signals, a hundred times a day. But so do men, and men also use another language which is symbolic and highly sophisticated.

Well? Where do we go then from here? Which way do we

start afresh? Suggestions pour in from all countries and all areas of activity.

De Haan suggests, for example, that a baby dolphin, isolated from his mother since birth, should be brought up only in contact with human beings so that he would learn to talk, not Dolphinese, but human language, somewhat like the reported wolf-child in India, who had acquired the habits of carnivores, ran on all fours, hunted with the pack, and grunted rudimentary language of canines; restored to human society when fully grown, he was never able to learn the language and ways of men. With dolphins this is practically impossible. The young *Tursiops* suckles for more than eight months, and lives glued to its mother for at least one and a half years. Lilly took a very young animal, no longer a baby, away from its mother, fed it from a bottle, but it died after several months despite continual care.

The reverse is not any easier. Place a human baby in water with dolphins? His chances for survival are nil for a thousand reasons having nothing to do with dolphins, and besides, even if a human child did learn Dolphinese in that way, we would not be able, once he had returned to land, to talk to him any more than to wolf-children or real dolphins.

Perhaps we could try to teach them languages other than English? They speak some Russian, we know that. A dolphin in the Black Sea correctly pronounced 'Mama' in Russian, and some other simple words, and these were recorded by Mrs Ekaterina Chichkova at the Hydro-Acoustics Laboratory of the Oceanographic Institute of the U.S.S.R. Personally I suggest Greek and Latin, for the most perfect harmony existed long ago between dolphins and men who spoke these languages.

Dr Bateson believes that the conversation of dolphins, as of all mammals, is not about facts or specific concepts, but about relationships between one individual and another, about social relations in general and about the rules which govern these relations.

He quotes these two examples: when a kitten asks its mistress for milk, it does not mime the word 'milk' but it plays the role of a tiny unhappy neglected animal, and acts out the word

109

'mama' or more exactly the word 'dependence'. It is up to the mistress to deduce from the situation, from her reciprocal relations with the cat as acted by it, that the cat wants milk. In the same way, when an old wolf, the head of the pack, wants to put down a rather too independent young male for showing interest in his females, he seizes his head in his jaws and forces it to the ground several times. This is exactly the system employed by adult wolves who wish to signify to the growing cub that the age for being suckled is past and that it is time to eat meat. The signal acted out by the head of the pack is therefore one with a pre-established sense, a metaphorical message from adult to cub, which means not 'Don't do that' but 'I'm your elder and boss.' When this happens the young wolf will do well in the future to understand that the leader's females are not for neophytes.

Bateson believes that dolphins communicate, not by gestures, mimicry or attitudes invisible in water but by sounds which constitute a vocabulary of relationships rather than a vocabulary of words. He believes that they exchange combinations of signals about these relationships from which each must then deduce for his own benefit the immediate practical applications.

This would fit in with the 'domination signal' of the female porpoise which Busnel mentions, but hardly with the thousand examples where cetaceans transmit precise, concrete information, such as the presence of a little harpoon gun at the bow of Norwegian whalers, as killer whales have been seen to do.

What does the syntax of a symbolic language resemble if the symbolic metaphors are for social relationships? We have no idea. Bateson thinks it may be organized along the lines of music. To understand such a system it is first necessary, he says, to understand the individual and general relationships between the animals, by observing their social life. One must next find out the origin of the metaphors signifying 'dependence' and 'domination', in other words, determine the context of each type vocalization. Once we have understood that, we shall be able to analyse and classify each context and ultimately subject them to the classic statistical methods of interpretation.

Dr Aronson thinks that if dolphins are as intelligent as some people think one must expect that the content of their message varies greatly according to the personal experience of each individual. In that case it would be necessary to select carefully the dolphins with whom one tries to enter into conversation, so as not to risk choosing the village idiot or some dull representative of the common herd rather than the genius, the sage, or the scholar of the band. Lilly, indeed, found out that old dolphins use a much larger vocabulary of signals than young ones; the fewer teeth they have left, the more elaborate is their command of language.

Still another possibility: perhaps it is not only sound which carries meaning, but also the intervals between sounds. Thorpe has observed the behaviour of the African shrike: in this species the responses of the female to the male are made at constant intervals and the information (which is simply the mutual recognition of the partners) is based on the lapse of time which separates the beginning of the theme sung by the male from the beginning of the theme sung by the female. In the same way, for the grey goose, it is the number of identical sounds per unit of time which determines the meaning of the message. Lawrence, who has observed the flight of birds, has discovered this law: the smaller the number of syllables, the greater the desire of the group to fly away. When geese cackle for more than five syllables it means they are happy where they are; less than five syllables means disquiet, they stop feeding and begin to move; at three syllables the movements become faster; at two syllables they prepare to fly away and one syllable is the final signal for immediate departure of the flock. Busnel, from whom I take all these examples, suggests that certain sequences of repetitive pilot whale signals recorded in the Mediterranean could be of this type. Are they really? He does not believe that we can determine this clearly with the type of analysis employed to date to decode human languages.

He does not believe either that we will ever be able to apply to dolphin language the purely mathematical methods in use for decoding tablets engraved in ancient languages. This method, based on analysis of the frequency of use of a symbol and the computation of its combinations, was used by Shirokov in 1962 to decipher Maya hieroglyphs. Dreher and Evans have tried to apply it to dolphin talk by simply relating their oscillograms to ideograms or hieroglyphs, but we have seen how contestable their sonograms are.

Busnel also proposes to look outside the realm of biology. There are, for example, diagrams very similar to oscillograms, which have been deciphered. He refers here to the recent analysis of musical documents written in Georgia in the eighth and ninth centuries and now preserved on Mount Athos, where the notes are indicated in a primitive way by pen-strokes whose form indeed recalls Dreher's markings. Could not the methods of decoding these signs be useful in the interpretation of Dolphinese? Toying with ideas and suggestions is exciting.

S. G. Wood, a military delphinologist, wonders if the sound world of the dolphin could not be entirely beyond our comprehension anyway, as alien to us as the olfactory world of the dog. Perhaps, he says, the sounds we produce in water with our machines do not have the meaning for the animal which we suppose them to have?

For myself, I have wondered if one could not learn a lot about dolphins by studying more closely the tomtom communications of some Africans, or the extraordinary way which they have of communicating from a great distance by modulated whistles barely audible to most Europeans. And here it is Busnel again who makes a fascinating suggestion, perhaps the most constructive of all: besides Africa, we know several countries where men employ a whistled language in addition to their normal language – the Mazataco Indians, for example, in Mexico (described by Gowan), the inhabitants of Silbo-Gomero in the Canaries, and those of Kuskoy in Turkey. Kuskoy literally 'the village of the birds', is a small village lost in the mountains along the Black Sea. The whistled language of the people of Kuskoy is many centuries old, and they have reached such mastery of their art that their whistles can be heard at more than five miles (the alarm signal of the sperm-whale carries, under water, for nine miles). Parents teach it to their children and even in the village school they learn to whistle at the same time as they learn to speak Turkish.

But another of these whistled languages which has been studied more closely, again by René Guy Busnel, is that of the village of Aas in the French Pyrenees; like that of Silbo-Gomero it is based on the Spanish language and more precisely on a Bearnese dialect. Oscillograms of this human whistled language are extraordinarily similar to those of the whistlings of the Odontoceti, each being characterized by typical modulation in frequency and amplitude. The scales of frequency are sometimes different, but there are also examples of whistlings on the same wave-lengths. The human signal is often longer, but not always.

The interesting fact here is that the people of Aas, to produce these whistlings, do not use their vocal cords but an apparatus quite similar to that of dolphins. Busnel has taken X-ray films of these whistlers in action. What do they do? First of all, they push the middle of their tongue backwards with a finger in order to secure a fixed position for it and so obtain great precision in the movements of the tip of the tongue. They thus form a pocket of air in the back of the throat, with which they play, using little modulations produced by the tip of the tongue; the larynx is motionless (the vocal cords do not vibrate) and plays the role of a piston. Now we often see the lips of a dolphin's blowholes moving in rapid vibrations. These vibrations must be caused by the pulmonary air under pressure, since the lips of the blowholes have no muscles and probably it is the two lips of the animal's glottis which are used to produce mechanical vibrations and to modulate the passage of air, just as the tongue of the whistler does.

We know that, under water, dolphins produce noises by using a set of sacs controlled by a complex system of specialized muscles. Busnel has tried to produce dolphin sounds by keeping the mouth and nostrils closed, and expelling no air. The oscillograms of these attempts show modulations in frequency, bitonal curves, sudden interruptions of frequency and a series of impulses, which are all characteristics of dolphins' oscillograms. Busnel produced these variations in frequency by increasing or diminishing the volume of the larynx and thorax cavities where the air resonates. With a little practice one can so modulate words of several syllables. This is only to show that the human larynx and its vocalizing apparatus is capable, under the same physical conditions as those of the dolphin (that is, without expelling air), of producing sounds which are similar in their acoustic properties. The constructive aspect of all this is that it could well turn out to be easier to teach a dolphin a whistled language than our usual voiced language.

Will whistlers from Turkey, Mexico or the Canaries soon be put in contact with dolphins? And will they perhaps find a basis of understanding more easily?

6   The Challenge to Hydrodynamics

Hydrodynamics has its laws, binding and unavoidable laws which are the Bible of naval construction engineers. But the Eucreodonts had not heard of them when they chose the ocean. Free from such considerations, the uninhibited dolphins still swim in their marine kingdom three times faster than is mathematically possible.

If one computes according to the rules the quantity of energy necessary to propel in sea-water a solid body in the form of a torpedo or a dolphin, and the quantity of energy a dolphin can deploy in terms of the quantity of energy normally produced by mammalian muscle per kilogram of weight, then one finds out that its top speed cannot exceed ten to twelve knots. However, as Pliny, the naturalist, said: 'The dolphin is swifter than a bird and he hurls himself forward in the water faster than an arrow launched from a powerful machine.'

However, as Belon said:

It is not without good reason that dolphins have been said to be the animals which surpass all others in speed, not only those which dwell in the sea but also those which are on the land; for, similarly, Aristotle says that he heard marvels about them and most incredible things – which things I have well seen for myself when being on various kinds of ships of the navy and in various seas on which we were bound to sail to go from one isle or country towards another, where we have seen the dolphins go faster than our ship could, whilst having all sails deployed and a fresh wind from behind, in such a way they would overtake us all the time.

However, as Lacépède said:

The Dolphin swims most frequently and with great speed ... the apparatus which gives him such high speed is composed of the tail and its terminal fluke, divided in two lobes. This fluke together with the tail itself may be moved with great strength, as the powerful muscles which power them lean on the upper apophyses of the lumber vertebrae, and such was the impression given by their prodigious strength that according to Rondelet, a proverb compared those men who sought to achieve something impossible to those who wanted to catch a dolphin by its tail. ... My learned and eloquent colleague the Citoyen de Saint-Pierre, member of the Institut National, says in the relation of his voyage to the Isle de France that he saw a dolphin prancing around the vessel whilst the ship was doing one myriameter per hour.

However, a U.S. Navy captain, when perfectly sober, saw in 1963 a school of porpoises swimming playfully round his destroyer, which was making thirty-two knots. The fact was entered in the logbook.

Furthermore other unofficial reports mention top speeds of 21, 40, 55 and even 60 knots. Johannesen and Harder, in 1960, saw an adult killer-whale doing 30 knots as it approached their ship, which was going at 20.6 knots, and then circle it for twenty minutes.

For the U.S. Navy, whose ships and torpedoes crawl along (if you consider the power of their engines and their fuel consumption), it was a challenge, an affront. To clear up the matter and take up the challenge, the Navy entrusted the investigation to its special services in California: the U.S. Naval Ordnance Test Station at China Lake, and the Naval Missile Center, Point Mugu. The military hydrodynamicists, helped by civilian researchers, conducted a long series of experiments, which they enormously complicated with the benevolent collaboration of Notty, a Pacific striped dolphin (*Lagennorhynchus obliquidens*). In an experimental tank, three hundred feet long but very shallow (barely six feet), belonging to General Dynamics, Convair Division of San Diego, Notty, who had apparently not the slightest reason to hurry, never exceeded fifteen knots. Besides his speed, the investigators measured his accelerations or decelerations, and the resistance to displacement of his body, with variations obtained by having him wear braking-collars of various diameters. They calculated scores of coefficients based on his weight, measurements, volume and horse-power output; they drew curves and graphs and then concluded (I quote Thomas G. Lang, who published the findings of the experiments):

The results of the tests on the dolphin Notty do not show any exceptional hydrodynamic or physical performance. The conditions of the tests, however, suggest that the hydrodynamic performances were considerably hindered by one of several factors of the environment ... the excessive turbulence of the water due to the formation of waves by the animal swimming too close to the surface (small depth), the small dimensions of the pool and their inhibiting influence ... all these factors indicate that the best place for performance tests of the kind would be ... the natural environment, the ocean.

After this inconclusive attempt the Office of Naval Research gave Dr Kenneth Norris, head of the Oceanic Institute, Sea Life Park, in Hawaii, a research contract to perform a similar series of experiments, this time out at sea. This was to be one of the first instances where a tame dolphin would be released in the high sea, free from all bounds, free not to return.

A special ten-week training course taught Keiki, a young *Tursiops gilli*, to reply to the 'come back' signal emitted under water, and to the 'overtake' signal emitted when Keiki, who followed a launch with 90 h.p. outboard motor, was to overtake it and to charge forward at top speed. A few mullets, as always, rewarded the correct reaction. Ten times in a row, in the open sea, on a 350-yard stretch between two buoys, young Keiki, who was enjoying himself immensely, overtook the boat. The boat was lightened to gain speed until it reached its peak at twenty knots, or thirty-seven km. per hour; Keiki was always ahead, impatient, it seemed, at the slowness of his playmates.

Norris now suspects that Keiki belongs to a particularly slow species. Two trained leopard dolphins, Haina and Nuha, have since exceeded twenty-one knots in front of a faster boat. Others attained twenty-six knots, and that is not the end; the experi-

117

ments continue and there are more than a hundred species of dolphins, porpoises and small Odontoceti. So what are the secrets, since secrets there are? Such secrets interest the torpedo manufacturers and submarine builders not only of the United States, but also of the U.S.S.R.

Firstly, as explained by Dr Irving Rehman of the University of California, a consultant to the Naval Ordnance Test Station, dolphins have learned to control turbulence, that is, the eddies which form around all solid bodies moving through water and slow them – this had been suspected for a long time, because dolphins are the only swimmers that do not leave any wake behind them. Except when surfacing to breathe, they cut through the water without wasting energy in shaking it. On photographs of a dolphin in movement, made under water by Essapian, one sees clearly that the skin is creased by waves perpendicular to the direction of swimming. Essapian believes that these waves are stationary and do not progress in a swell-like motion, which would be the case if due to turbulence and produced by the movement of swimming. Unlike a ship's bottom, he says, the soft malleable surface of a dolphin's body bends and adjusts itself to each tiny local variation in water pressure around it. This is of extreme importance because turbulent waters offer seven times more resistance to movement than 'smooth' waters with a laminar flow. This being understood, the next question: 'And how do they manage it?' becomes more complicated.

'Their skin is quite special,' Messieurs Brechet and Roussel de Vauzème had already stated in the knowledgeable paper which they read in 1834 to the Académie des Sciences in Paris. They had very well observed its characteristics and very wrongly interpreted them.

Professor Gray of Cambridge University, comparing the amount of energy furnished with the resistance of the water to a given form, that of a dolphin, concluded in 1938: 'It would not seem that there is any reason to believe that the form or surface of a whale, a dolphin or an inert fish bestows on the body a notably different resistance from that of a well streamlined object of comparable size and speed.' According to him, it is movement which avoids turbulence, it is the flexion movement of the rear part of the body, and above all, the sinusoidal trajectory of the tail.

Dolphins have an extremely soft satin-like skin, and it is irrigated, according to Rehman, who has studied many microscopic slides of it, by a multitude of papillae which contain tiny blood-vessels, very close to the epidermis. In response to each beginning of an eddy, these blood-vessels could possibly discharge locally and very rapidly (under the muscular control of the animal, which inflates or contracts them) enough heat to supply a variation of volume and output of calories that would produce a miscroscopic film of water of lower viscosity (therefore smooth and not turbulent) on the animal's skin. This histological particularity is most noticeable where the wake should normally be the strongest, that is, on the rear of the body, on the bottom side of the flippers and the fluke. Is it a system which envelops the dolphin in a portable and invisible film of calm water, of which the laminar flow offers one seventh

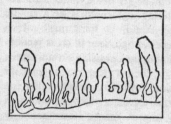

Fig. 7. A comparison under the microscope between two slices of a dolphin's skin, one taken between the eye and the snout (left), the other taken from the ventral face of the tail fluke. It can be seen that the complexity, number and size of the dermic papillae which contain blood vessels become greater nearer the tail, i.e. where the potential turbulence becomes greater; they also appear to become closer to the external layer of the skin. This is believed to be part of the physiological system used by the dolphin to prevent any incipient water turbulence: by locally deflecting his outer skin and by modifying his local skin temperature in answer to slight local over pressures. (U.S. Navy documents.)

of the resistance encountered by a torpedo of the same volume? Rehman suggests it could be, but pending experimental evidence he makes no affirmations yet.

Nothing being simple in cetology, another researcher, the German Max O. Kramer, attributes to dolphins a different technique for reaching the same result. This he also bases on observations of microscopic sections of a dolphin's skin where, as far as he is concerned, he sees a quite different arrangement. Kramer after the war was crossing the Atlantic on his way to the United States, where he was going to live, when he was struck by the effortless ease of some dolphins playing around the liner. That reminded him of something: a patent which he had taken out in 1938 in Berlin while he was working for the Ministry of Aeronautics. His patent proposed to remedy the oscillations in current of fluids passing at close proximity to a rigid wall, by means of a layer of thin, tightly packed wires attached to the wall in the direction of flow. In 1955 Kramer examined sections of dolphin cutaneous tissue under a microscope. He observed in the exterior pigmented layer a supple flexible envelope, bulging with liquid, $1\frac{1}{2}$ mm. thick, which covered the harder dermis. This envelope, seen in cross-section, would consist of an exterior diaphragm pressing on numerous tiny vertical water-filled spongy ducts (water makes up four fifths of the weight of the skin). And he concluded that the dolphin, applying the basic principle of his 1938 patent, with extreme refinement and many improvements, instantaneously replied by inflexions of his spongy skin to the slightest exterior pressure recorded by the hypersensitive diaphragm of his epidermis.

We know that a laminar flow can be maintained for ever by a comparable mechanical system. R. Betchov, a researcher of Douglas Aircraft, experimentally demonstrated this in 1959.

Kramer himself has built an artificial model of a dolphin's skin with two sandwiched layers of rubber with a network of tiny flexible canals filled with liquid in between. By coating a rigid model four feet long with this flexible envelope he has succeeded in reducing by 60 per cent the braking effect in an experimental tank caused by turbulence in a forty-knot current.

Commercial applications are now being considered not only for submarines and torpedoes, but also for pipelines and water ducts. The U.S. Navy has toyed with the idea of equipping its ships with the system, but there still are the problems of the air-water interface and, for submarines, the problem of rubber ageing. Above all marine growth and barnacles would quickly settle on the coating, a problem unknown to the dolphin, whose skin rapidly regenerates.

Kramer has received much publicity since he published his discovery in 1960. So has U.S. Rubber, producers of LAMI-FLOT coating, a flexible lining which reduces by 27 per cent the water friction on a ship's bottom, and so has shipowner Stavros Niarchos since he proposed to equip a new yacht with it. But there has not been much said about a new science, 'Bionics', inspired by the dolphins, which simulates living forms in turning nature's inventions to man's benefit; nor about its true pioneers, the Russian Yuri Aleev of the Ukrainian Academy of Sciences at Sebastopol, and, above all, Professor Auguste Piccard.

Because, if we are to render to Caesar what belongs to Caesar, then we must bring back from oblivion an article entitled 'Der Delphin unser Lehrmeister (*Neue Zürcher Zeitung*, 6 July 1949), in which Auguste Piccard first suggests that we could draw profit from the secrets of the dolphin; and another article, published a little later in the Belgian newspaper *Le Soir*, where he predicted for the future: 'A liner powered by a quite ordinary small diesel, which would hardly consume more fuel than two or three lorry engines, and which would cross the Atlantic in thirty-six hours at half price without rolling or pitching, since it would sail 100 feet below the surface.' The name of this submarine of the future was of course the *Dolphin*. (Piccard was to develop his idea again in greater detail in 1954 in a chapter of his book *Au fond des mers en bathyscaphe*.)

Trying his hand at scientific anticipation the professor explained in the voice of the imaginary captain of the submarine *Dolphin*:

The easy-to-observe fact that the dolphin does not produce waves proves that he possesses a secret which allows for an economy that

121

no naval engineer has ever been able to achieve. ... If the dolphin does not produce waves it is because he does not create eddies, or rather that he destroys the least wave that is in danger of forming. To do that he needs some special devices. He must register the slightest irregularity of pressure announcing the formation of an eddy, he must know exactly what is the movement of his skin which will destroy this eddy and finally, he must execute this movement immediately. All this the dolphin does and very rapidly. The sensitive nerves located under the skin inform him of the pressures; his brain, or if you prefer his instinct or his subconscious, calculates the necessary action, the motor nerves give the order to the muscles which execute the required movements. ... We have imitated him. A number of small pressure gauges are distributed through the rubber membrane which covers the hull of our *Dolphin*; electric wires communicate the readings of the gauges to the electronic computer which some of you have just seen. By a second network of

Fig. 8. The sinusoidal path of the dolphin's tail and fluke. (U.S. Navy document.)

wires this artificial brain sends out electric currents to numerous small electric magnets placed beneath the skin of the *Dolphin* and these magnets, while slightly displacing the skin, immediately neutralize the smallest forming eddy. It's very simple.

The only true difficulty consisted in finding the laws by which the surface of the vessel should react to the variations in pressure. We worked on this in the laboratory for five years and you now see the result.

Without the slightest eddy, having to overcome only the slight and inevitable resistance due to the viscosity of the water our ship crosses the Atlantic and tomorrow morning it will surface opposite the Statue of Liberty.

The question of turbulence aside, there are other devices which further improve the performance of the dolphin. He has not merely reduced the resistance to forward movement, he has also multiplied his production of energy. The muscles of cetaceans contain three times more myoglobin than those of other

122

animals. Myoglobin is truly a reservoir of oxygen which swells the muscular cells with fuel and multiplies their output. Like the haemoglobin of the blood, it is a red-pigmented substance which becomes loaded with oxygen, but myoglobin keeps its oxygen much longer. Haemoglobin distributes its fuel wherever the blood travels, wherever there is a need. Myoglobin is a reserve supply. When the supplies from the bloodstream are insufficient, when the need for oxygen in the muscle becomes almost desperate (in fact when the differences in oxygen tension in the pigment and in the muscular cell increases), and only then, the myoglobin begins to discharge its oxygen. We know today that physical training brings about a rise in the quantity of haemoglobin stored in the muscles of athletes in tiptop condition. Dolphins, in the course of their evolution, have certainly trained hard.

Last, from a purely mechanical point of view, the beating of the horizontal rudder which constitutes the fluke propels the cetacean much more efficiently than the propeller of a torpedo or a submarine; a propeller takes water from the sides, changes its direction by an angle of ninety degrees and pushes it backwards with an extreme waste of energy. The tail of the dolphin only displaces the water streams by thirty degrees; its effectiveness is therefore definitely superior.

7

Decompression? What For?

When birds, reptiles and mammals became divers, their internal organs changed as much, in the course of evolution, as their outer aspect did.

For all, the basic adaptations are identical because the demands made by the new, denser and non-breathable environment have determined the selection of survivors. The animal must be able to descend beneath the surface and function there efficiently for a long time. On top of that the pinnipeds and the cetaceans, which dive much deeper than the cormorants, crocodiles, otters or other semi-aquatic forms, have acquired some unusual tricks for coping with the peculiar dangers of deep-diving. Now these tricks of theirs are of enormous interest to me personally, since I lack them and have had, therefore, more than my fair share of 'the bends', though I spent days and weeks of my life sitting in a metal box being slowly decompressed.

The two main characteristics common to all scaled, feathered or furry divers are an adjustment of the respiratory reflexes and a slowing down of the heartbeat.

Breathing: the nerve cells of the brain which induce respiration by giving the animal a feeling of suffocation, go into action when a certain quantity of carbon dioxide builds up in the blood around them. The warning, however, is given well in advance of any really dangerous lack of oxygen. In the diving mammals, these controlling nerve cells have become much less sensitive than that of their landlubber counterparts, so that they can take a much greater concentration of the CO_2 which accumulates in the blood when breathing is suspended. This, by the way, is what all trained spear-fishermen also do; they have learned to fight and control their breathing reflex, which is not always done without risk.

Heartbeat: a century ago the great French physiologist, Paul Bert, had already noticed that a duck's heartbeat slowed down considerably when the bird went under water. Since then the same slowing down has been shown to take place in all aquatic birds, reptiles and mammals as soon as they dive or simply stick their heads in the water. This, in fact, is more a specialized adaptation of a general characteristic than a novelty with survival value, as it can be observed as well among all land animals that are accidentally submerged.

Accordingly, when a penguin dives, its heartbeat drops from 200 to 20 beats a minute. That of certain seals drops from 120 to 10 as soon as their nostrils touch water; that of the beaver goes from 140 to 20; that of the white whale from 30 to 16; that of the *Tursiops* dolphin from 110 to 45 and that of a pearl-diver or spear-fisherman, after one minute of bottom-time, from 72 to 35. Yet, although the heartbeat and, therefore, the flow of blood, slows up, the arterial pressure does not fall, thus proving a considerable vascular constriction (this has been demonstrated experimentally in seals), which cuts off the circulation to limbs and organs of lesser priority in order to concentrate the oxygen load of the blood in the places where it is indispensable – in the heart and brain; this mechanism is also used by the body in case of shock or severe haemorrhage.

Conversely, this same rationing phenomenon takes place when a flying-fish 'dives' out of the water into the air or when a human baby, or an infant seal, makes its plunge into the atmosphere from its aquatic environment in the uterus.

By specific adaptations pinnipeds and cetaceans have developed even further this technique of saving oxygen for top-priority organs. They have developed two special devices for local concentration of blood: first, the posterior vena cava is unusually large and at the level of the diaphragm contains a sphincter muscle which regulates the flow of blood and maintains a sort of reserve of oxygenated blood; second, they keep a supply of fresh blood in the thorax and around the brain in special 'sponges'. These sponges, called retia mirabilia or 'marvellous networks', were already recorded by Belon, though he did not understand their function. But in the nineteenth century Cuvier did understand:

The heart of dolphins and whales does not appear to have undergone important changes through evolution; but the circulatory system presents very important modifications in the form of infinite circumvolutions of the arteries. ... A network of blood vessels, filled with oxygenated blood, is thereby created, which are mostly located on both sides of the spine, under the pleura between the ribs. The arteries which make up these networks are offshoots of the arteries situated between the ribs. All these arteries have a common origin in the area above the pectoral aorta and run into the rachidian canal and even enter the skull through the occipital aperture. These blood vessels are not formed by anastomosed branches; one may unfold them, so to speak, as if they were formed from one great vein a thousand times folded back on itself; and in addition to their main connection with the arteries between the ribs, they also hook up with the vertebral and carotid arteries. Presumably the unique complexity of these blood vessels is caused by the necessity which the cetaceans often have of suspending their breathing for prolonged periods and, therefore, suspending the oxygenation of their blood. These numerous arteries become a reservoir of oxygenated blood which is slowly put back in circulation and sustains the animal's life when the venous blood would mean only death.

What Cuvier assumed, following the views of Hunter and Breschet, was confirmed by Erikson in 1940: he theorized that the retia mirabilia functioned as artery-to-vein connections, which during underwater activity permitted the blood to avoid the muscles and go straight to the large vein trunks. This hypothesis still has not been proved anatomically, although the 'marvellous networks' have been described today with great precision. The most important of them, extending on both sides of the spinal column and between the ribs, is the thoracic retia, formed by two small branches from the aorta and the intercostal arteries; according to Grassé it fits neatly into the vein-

126

system of the thorax and, taken as a whole, appears like a spongy tissue in a mass of fat. Another network surrounds the brain, drawing from the spinal arteries which join up closely with the thoracic retia.

Once again, these 'marvellous networks' are superb examples of evolution's flexibility. They are no new pieces of equipment, they are only a selective adaptation of an organ common to many animals. Dogs and wolves have retia in the pads on the soles of their feet, which are often exposed to intense cold, and the retia, no doubt, warm them up by furnishing a greater flow of blood. Sloths and other mammals which spend their life upside-down, hanging from a branch by hands and feet, have them also, possibly for the opposite purpose, to keep all the blood from ending up in their heads and organs.

The combination of these different systems in the seal, for example, is so effective that his oxygen consumption when under water is reduced by four fifths.

Furthermore, the cetaceans get much more efficiency from their lungs than we do, theirs being proportionately half as big as ours. We humans only renew 15 to 20 per cent of our lung contents with each breath, whereas a dolphin, whose expiration-inspiration cycle lasts only a fraction of a second, expels and stores about 90 per cent fresh air every time. From that inhaled air the dolphin extracts 10 per cent of the 21 per cent of oxygen it contains, while our lungs extract a meagre 5 to 6 per cent at most. In short, the dolphin, by breathing in three times more air than we do and extracting from it twice as much oxygen, profits six times more than we do from every breath he takes.

So there is no secret really, no miracle is involved, only a complex system of multiple adaptations which function simultaneously.

Yet all this does not explain how cetaceans manage to reach record depths and come back alive. Physiologists and deep-diving specialists continue to scratch their heads. Nitrogen narcosis? The bends? All those dangers which thwart men's penetration of the ocean depths are disdainfully ignored by our cousins the cetaceans.

As every whaler knows, male sperm whales can remain under

water for an hour or an hour and a half. Before they dive they will take one breath for each minute they will stay submerged, and the old-time harpooners used to say: 'Sperm whale of sixty tons that breathes in sixty times will stay down sixty minutes.' Since the animal generally kept the same course under water, they could predict where and when he would surface, and they were never wrong.

The old whaling captains also used to claim that a fully grown sperm whale could dive to 3,000 or 5,000 feet. And if they made such claims, it was because they often saw the old

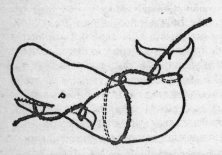

Fig. 9. Carcass of a drowned sperm whale raised from a depth of 3,302 feet off Ecuador by a cable-laying ship with the telegraphic cable in which it had become entangled. Other sperm whales have died the same way when becoming fouled in cables lying in depths of 3,850 feet. (After Heezen, 1957.)

harpooned males empty out three 'tubs' of line, i.e. three wooden pans containing 220 yards each of wound-up line. Three tubs was 600 fathoms or 1,108 metres which the animal unrolled vertically before reappearing at the same spot where he had gone under. The young or female whales plunged less deep for less time, took more breaths to begin with, and hardly ever unrolled more than a tub and a half (300 fathoms).

Of course the armchair scholars, with their knowledgeable opinions, would refuse to believe 'legends' of that sort and stated quite clearly that such pressures (1,600 pounds on every square inch of the body at 600 fathoms) would kill any creature.

Yet in 1935 the cable-laying ship *All America* fished up the forty-five foot carcase of an old male which had entangled itself, alive, in an underwater cable 3,302 feet down. Since then a dozen other similar cases have been substantiated; the deepest being a jaw of a sperm whale caught in a cable at a depth of 1,145 metres (3,850 feet). Dr Heezen, who has published the results of his thorough and accurate survey of all these cases, suggests that the cetaceans got themselves entangled in the cables while they were swimming at these great depths with their mouths open in pursuit of squid which they feed on.

That cables can attract hungry creatures is well understood by all divers who have seen how a cable lost on the muddy bottom maintains, like a sunken wreck, a teeming living community which festers and feeds on each other in closed circuit.

And yet we still read in an authoritative treatise on zoology published in Paris in 1955: 'The accounts which claim that certain Balaenoptera have hurt themselves, after being harpooned, when hitting the bottom at depths of over 500 metres (1,675 feet) or that sperm whales have strangled themselves with underwater cables at great depths, cannot be considered genuine ...' and on another page we can read about these 'great whales acquainted with depths of 100 metres (330 feet!) and more'.

The whale with the greatest underwater endurance, perhaps, is not the sperm whale but rather the small beaked whale, *Hyperodon rostratus*. Once harpooned it may remain two hours under water. Moving about, it makes routine dives of one hour all day long. The blue and grey whales when fully grown can reach three thousand feet for a short excursion, or they can stay under about an hour at shallow depth; baby whales do not dive very deep and neither do the smaller cetaceans, including dolphins and porpoises.

For a long time it was believed that the porpoise could not go any deeper than two hundred feet and the dolphin three hundred. But Professor Conrad Neumann (of the Institute of Marine Sciences, University of Miami), during a recent descent of the research submarine *Aluminaut*, has seen through the portholes curious dolphins watching him from outside at three hundred feet and at six hundred feet he could hear their beep-beep, quite near the hull, it seemed.

Scientifically to determine the limits of cetaceans' capacities, Professor Baldwin, who heads the Sensory Systems Laboratory at Tucson, Arizona, proposes to use biotelemetry, i.e. the techniques which allow us to measure most physiological reactions of man or animal at a distance, without changing natural conditions in any way during the experiment. 'Space quality' miniaturized electronic and electrical equipment has made possible this new kind of espionage, which renders miraculous service to medicine, physiology, biology, zoology and even the police. Biotelemetry enabled Dr Norris, in 1964, to carry out his first recordings on tame dolphins let loose out at sea. Since then such recordings have become routine: electrocardiograms, taking internal temperatures, studying the digestive tract, sound detection, clocking speeds, checking the depths attained, etc.

Thus Dr Kooyman (University of Arizona) discovered that Weddell seals can dive deeper than 1,430 feet beneath the ice (1,000 feet was the routine depth for fifty successive dives); that they stayed under as long as twenty-eight minutes and came back to the air-hole they started from; or even that they could cruise beneath the ice from one hole to another one as far off as one mile away. At first Dr Kooyman attached an ultrasonic transmitter (45–55 kilocycles) to the seal's neck. The transmitter's wave-length varied according to the depth reached by the seal, and the doctor could follow the animal's course with a submerged directional receiver. Later he equipped his subjects with tiny bathymetric recording clocks.

These experiments resulted in a total upset of many ideas concerning pinnipeds, which were supposed according to the books 'to hunt only in shallow waters'. They also suggested new questions. Scholander once put young seals through a simulated dive in a hyperbaric chamber. He sent them 'down' to 250 feet and brought them 'up' in perfect shape. However, when he had them 'go down' to 1,000 feet and then 'brought them up', they suffered decompression sickness (the bends). Do seals then know their own decompression tables? And when they dive by themselves, at sea, do they come up in stages, waiting the prescribed number of minutes at each stop?

A *Steno brendanensis* dolphin, named Kai, reached 135 feet during a rehearsal of such a test but unfortunately (or for him fortunately?) he then chose freedom and left Dr Norris to himself, marooned in his launch under the scenic Hawaiian cliffs. At Point Mugu a harnessed dolphin has dived to 550 feet, under Navy control – the round trip took him 2.45 minutes. Norris has since begun training other dolphins of tractable disposition, particularly a certain Pono, who is getting used to a special harness rigged up with a depth gauge and other instruments and is being taught to swim straight down following an anchor chain. To prove he has reached bottom he will have to ring a bell attached to a sunken weight. Through other instruments to be attached to the harness, Norris will be able also to follow, and check at a distance, pulmonary functions and blood circulation, and even to record an electrocardiogram which he will study in connection with the varying depths reached. Will all this finally explain the cetacean's remarkable immunity from 'the bends'?

Decompression accidents, the 'bends', which can paralyse or kill a man, are due to the formation of gas bubbles in the blood or in the tissues of a diver who comes up from a too-long or too-deep dive too fast to allow the inert gas (nitrogen or helium), dissolved in his body under bottom pressure, to be turned back into gas and naturally eliminated through the lungs. In his blood the same thing happens as happens when you pop the cork of a champagne bottle; whereas in the blood of a diver decompressed according to the rules, the same thing happens as happens with an improperly capped bottle, 'flat' when opened because it has lost its gas and pressure slowly, without a single bubble ever forming.

Helmet divers or scuba divers breathe compressed air or gas delivered at ambient pressure, but some Polynesian skin-divers, who dive to a hundred feet twenty to forty times a day with no breathing equipment at all (just like cetaceans) and stay under one or two minutes each time looking around for mother-of-pearl, are often stricken with a sickness they call 'tarawana' and cannot explain.

Tarawana has recently been studied, on the spot, by several groups of physicians who give it another name, 'decompression accidents'. What happens is this: each time the mother-of-pearl diver goes down, he carries in his lungs about five litres of air. During the two minutes he spends down his blood, which is normally saturated with nitrogen under surface pressure (one atmosphere), becomes loaded up with more nitrogen, now dissolved under four atmospheres (ambient pressure). This takes place with every heartbeat, every time his blood passes through the pulmonary alveoli, which function, in fact, as gas exchangers. The diver will then surface with just a little under five litres in his lungs, the missing volume being in a liquid state in his blood. If his dives follow one another too rapidly, the dissolved gas will not be entirely eliminated at the surface when he ventilates his lungs. The quantity of gas dissolved in his organism will increase little by little, dive after dive, until, after a particularly rapid surfacing, generally at the end of the day, the difference of tension between dissolved gas and pulmonary gas will be sufficiently high for the gas in the oversaturated blood to form into bubbles. Each dive, from that moment on, will make the diver's condition worse. Now, if a mammal who happens to be a Polynesian and a pearl-diver gets 'bent' after thirty two-minute dives at a hundred feet, how will any other mammal fare, even if he happens to be a marine one and a sperm whale, who goes down all day long to double or thirty times the depth and stays down ten to sixty times longer?

The zoologist Laurie, a member of the *Discovery* expedition, observed in 1933 that the blood and urine of captured cetaceans, when analysed, showed a very low percentage of dissolved nitrogen. He also noticed that the quantity of nitrogen dissolved in a pint of whale's blood first exposed to air (and therefore rapidly saturated at atmospheric pressure) and then isolated decreased little by little. This he attributed to aerobic bacteria, supposedly present in all cetaceans' blood, which would fix the nitrogen perhaps in much the same way as certain other bacteria which perform such a function in the roots of leguminous plants.

If that were true cetaceans would be equipped with an automatic regulatory mechanism for reducing nitrogen and thereby avoid the dangerous oversaturation that causes bubbles. 'However,' the late Professor J. S. Haldane reports, 'his later work has led Laurie to doubt that the regulatory agent is bacteria.' In fact he wondered if the famous bacteria had not invaded the blood after the animal's decease.

There is another hypothesis, more likely and more recent. When a sperm whale surfaces after a dive, his first breath shoots up twenty feet high with explosive force. It can be heard 250 yards away. The following breaths, much less violent, are still always visible because the whale ejects a sort of mist quite fetid as well and which burns a man's eyes and skin, as old harpooners will tell you. Fraser and Purves have wondered whether this breath is not a mist made of froth loaded with nitrogen. The sinuses of the sperm whale's skull contain enormous quantities of a stable, oily mucus, much more than the sinuses of the Mysticeti and the little Odontoceti, which dive less deep. The sperm whale in particular possesses, under its huge square brow, a special reservoir called a 'melon', filled with the famous 'spermaceti', a fine, light oil, formerly used by watchmakers. This, of course, is how he got his name. What is the purpose of a 'melon'? A protective bumper? A float? An acoustical device for picking up sonar signals? There is a wide choice of oversimplified theories. The most likely: the spermaceti which would go into the respiratory system in a mist form would absorb all or most of the dangerous dissolved nitrogen, which would then be expelled, during expiration, with the tiny oil-drops where it safely bubbles (for fats and oils do absorb six times more nitrogen than blood). By and large, moreover, it would seem that the quantity of oil found in all cetacean sinuses is in direct proportion to the depth and duration of their usual dives.

In any case, it is clear now that the whales' immunity to nitrogen accidents, narcosis and emboli, does depend on a whole range of complex factors which we just begin to suspect.

Scholander has explained another of their secrets: in the human diver, the lungs continue their function of gas exchangers at a reduced rate, even when they are compressed to one quarter of their surface volume. Circulation also goes on, considerably slowed down, however. But the lungs of deep-diving cetaceans are so compressed against their flexible ribs and thorax, between the diaphragm and the viscera, that the volume of the alveoli, where gas exchange takes place, is reduced to next to nothing.

Scholander tells us how. He has measured the pulmonary capacity of a seventy-ton whale; the lung volume was 2,000 litres; the volume of the dead spaces (i.e. the trachea and bronchi), 200 litres. When the whale dives to 100 metres or 333 feet (eleven atmospheres of pressure) the *whole* respiratory volume is forced into the non-compressible dead space of the respiratory tract, where gas diffusion is very slow. The lungs themselves are folded flat and just left out of circuit. Simultaneously, as we already know, blood circulation is slowed by two thirds, which further minimizes the absorption of the small quantity of gas that could be dissolved and limits sharply its diffusion from one body tissue to the others. But then a question immediately comes to mind. How do the cetaceans manage to feed their muscles their necessary quota of oxygen fuel during a dive?

This is their final secret.

When a human skin-diver hyperventilates his lungs by deep breathing before going down, he loads the haemoglobin of his blood with a reserve of oxygen equal to 41 per cent of the utilized oxygen and the myoglobin of his muscles with 13 per cent, while the balance goes to the lungs (34 per cent) and to the other body tissues (12 per cent). Whereas whales, with their lungs almost empty and the other body tissues not being irrigated, also store 41 per cent of their fuel in the blood, but they further pack an extraordinary 41 per cent more (according to Professor Slijper of Amsterdam University) in their myoglobin. In other words they leave the surface with three times as much fuel stored in their muscles as the best pearl-diver is able to take down in his.

8 The Intellectual of the Sea

In Chapter 5, dealing with dolphin language, we have had a foretaste of the dissensions that arise among dolphin experts when the subject of the superior intelligence of the dolphin is broached.

These arguments revolve round the cetaceans' neuro-cerebral equipment. The question was: What level of intelligence could dolphins possibly attain, judging from the faculties generally associated in mammals with such or such volume or particular characteristics of the brain?

Now let us approach the problem from the other end. Is there anything in their behaviour, as scientifically observed and verified, which demonstrates a certain intelligence? And, if so, what can we reasonably deduce from it?

In the discussion on anatomical grounds, there has been from the first no lack of big guns in the camp of those who oppose the superior intelligence theory. But this should not frighten us; there was no shortage either on the other side of equally eminent specialists, by no means less qualified, members of no less learned societies and authors of publications no less weighty. How are the forces balanced when it comes to the interpretation of cetacean behaviour?

The great Encyclopedists, strong in their ignorance, were writing, as late as the end of the last century: 'Their [dolphins'] intelligence seems rather dull, but the maternal instinct is highly developed.' On the other hand, a man like Frédéric Cuvier, after collating and analysing all that the science of his day could tell him on the subject, was of the opinion that 'Their behaviour exhibits a remarkable intellectual development,' and that 'of all the cetaceans the dolphins seem to have made the fullest use of their intellectual resources and appear to have the quickest and widest comprehension of environmental circumstances.' Which is not a bad definition of intelligence. A dictionary talking about definitions would read under the heading intelligence: 'the ability to know, to understand'. But definititions of intelligence made for man by man with reference to man fit better between the pages of men's dictionaries than in our discussion.

I, myself, prefer to believe that intelligence *per se*, Intelligence with a capital I, does not exist (not any more than Truth can be said to exist *per se*), and that what we are dealing with is an infinite number of different intelligences, as many as there are conscious beings. Now, as Reysenbach de Haan reminded us, 'Where there is language, there is consciousness.' He also considers it 'highly probable' that cetaceans have developed one or more complex language systems, an idea to which hundreds of instances lend irresistible support, and of which the psychologist Jarvis Bastian has recently produced experimental confirmation. Dolphins possess consciousness, and therefore intelligence. It is an intelligence which differs from our own in both essence and function, but such a difference implies absolutely no hierarchy, no idea of a 'higher' or 'lower' intelligence, for no objective criterion exists by which to measure their aims against ours, or the choice of means by which each group attempts, in its own situation, to achieve these aims. Cynics might argue: 'Come on, Mr Einstein, if you were *that* smart you'd be making more money a month!' In speaking of dolphins this attitude generally takes the form: 'They build nothing. They have created nothing'; or, 'Well, they haven't got television yet, have they?'

'To each its own intelligence,' Pirandello would say, and let us not try to class the dolphin higher or lower than a chimpanzee, a moron or the average man. Let us try, quite simply, without making any value judgements, to know and to describe the mind of the dolphin as it manifests itself in its day-to-day life.

It is those who have known the dolphin longest and best who entertain the greatest respect for its intelligence. The old whaling men, Herman Melville among them, knew that a sperm whale which has been harpooned and has survived will never again let itself be approached; they knew that an alarmed sperm whale would always make its escape by heading into the wind where no square-rigged ship can follow (in dead calm he would flee precisely towards the quarter from which the wind last blew); they knew that a whale can broadcast the alarm instantly six or seven miles around and that the rest of the herd would then either escape or (acting upon orders?) organize a rescue expedition.

Whalers learnt the usefulness of 'drag irons', special harpoons which would catch a baby sperm-whale without killing it immediately, thus giving the men time to harpoon the mother, and sometimes other females as well, while they were trying to break the line and free the young one.

It is the whalers also who told us how killer whales, if 'warned' by one of their number who had been wounded, can identify a harpoon-gun, and will keep well out of range of those ships, and only those, that carry one on their bow. Which suggests that they have somehow managed to communicate the warning to all members of the group, together with an account of the accident and a detailed description of the dangerous unknown object.

Do Mysticeti learn more slowly? It takes migratory grey whales several seasons before they learn to give a wide berth to whaling stations newly set up along the coast.

Among scientists, those who know the cetaceans otherwise than through books are basically in agreement, but with some shades of opinion. No need to repeat here Dr Lilly's credo; and Dr Kenneth Norris writes: 'As soon as contact was established with these creatures (dolphins), zoologists realized that they were animals of a very high relative intelligence.'

This contact had been lost since classical times and scientists owe its restoration to commercial undertakings like the Seaquarium, the Marine Studios, Marineland and other marine circuses. In his day, Frédéric Cuvier was already complaining that

137

Though some men have made the History of Animals the object of their study, they have only succeeded by chance in adding some few observations to those they have inherited from their predecessors; animals flee from us, and all too often it is only by taking their life that we bend them to our designs, and in so doing we take away the essential characteristic of their being. And if these difficulties beset the natural history of animals in general, how much the more do they make themselves felt in our dealings with the several species of cetaceans, those mammals who inhabit the widest and deepest oceans, whom we seek out only to engage in mortal combat, or who escape our endeavours by the speed and power of their motions, or who are cast up, half putrefied, on our shores by the operations of some distant freak of fortune.

And further on:

To the eyes of modern man the dolphin is merely a voracious carnivore, whose ends are solely those of feeding, rest and reproduction, and whose instincts serve no purpose other than the satisfaction of those needs. Yet, to the men of classical times, the dolphin was a gentle, good-natured and intelligent animal, most responsive to benevolent treatment. To strike a balance between opinions so diametrically opposed would necessitate a course of study which, in modern times, no man has even thought to undertake.

Today, at least, some men have thought to undertake such a study. But what foresight in this patriarch of delphinologists to anticipate, a century and a quarter before our time, all that we are now in the process of 'discovering' with such a fanfare of self-congratulations:

It does not behoove us to reject, as stories made merely for idle pleasure, all that is extraordinary in what the ancients relate on the subject of the dolphin. To my mind, we cannot but discover in these tales that these creatures are, on the intellectual plane, far different from what we suppose them; and that they offer to those who observe them a fountainhead of important truths which bear at once upon the study of the dolphin species and on the more perfect understanding of general psychology.

This 'fountainhead of important truths' now lies open to researchers, thanks to the modern producers of marine shows, which not only serve to relieve the boredom of the tourist but also offer to scientists unprecedented scope for observation and experiment.

In 1938, when a group of financiers, at the instigation of William Rolleston, founded the 'Florida Marineland' at St Augustine, few people thought the enterprise would make the grade. 'Pay to look at fish? You must be kidding.' There are now twelve marine circuses in the United States, all of which put on shows where dolphins play the star parts. There are others in Hawaii, South Africa, Europe and Australia. Everywhere they are crammed with customers.

The far-sighted Rolleston, however, was no innovator. Did he know that an ancient Greek business man, scenting potential profit in the friendship between his son (the boy from Poroselene, whom Oppian and Pausanias admired) and a dolphin of his own age, had encouraged their relationship so that it became, according to Aelianus, 'a spectacle for the diversion of visitors and a source of income to the child's parents'? And did he know that in the sixteenth century 'the inhabitants of Rimini in Italy, on the coasts of the Adriatic Sea, found a dolphin ... which was stranded and covered with sand, a quarter of a league from the town, which they loaded on a cart, still living, and brought it to Rimini where it remained alive the space of three days, and if it be true what they told me concerning it, those who brought it thus gained much profit from showing it, for whoever would see it had first to part with some piece of money.'

The Miami Seaquarium, with three different dolphin 'shows', its aquaria filled with every type of glittering tropical fish, its tiger-sharks, manatees and its jungle section, is without doubt the most remarkable of these spectacular modern super-attractions. Its Director of Public Relations, Roger Conklin, certainly deserves much of the credit for this success, and it is no little help to him in fulfilling his duties that he is himself so enthusiastic a lover of dolphins, of nature and of the sea, that he rallies the support of the most indifferent. It was Conklin in Miami who introduced me to Adolf Frohn.

Adolph Frohn, son, grandson and great-grandson of animal-

139 .

tamers, was born in a caravan in Hamburg. During the war he worked with sea-lions for Barnum and Bailey; but the war made it difficult to get a supply of these animals, so he moved to Marineland, where dolphins were kept in captivity. At that time the dolphins played only among themselves and for themselves, but Frohn, from the first, realized the use to which these games could be put, given suitable direction. He began to encourage their spontaneous play, and then to organize it. His first pupil, Flippy, had soon learned to push across the pool an attractive model seated on a raft. The public was enthusiastic.

Frohn, then, was the first producer – I would not say 'tamer' – to introduce dolphins in show business. 'Of all the animals I've worked with,' he told me, 'these are the ones who catch on quickest to what you want them to do.'

O. Feldman, trainer of the famous film-star Flipper, holds exactly the same opinion. 'As soon as I can get him to understand some new trick I want him to do, he does it, and he'll never forget. Six months later I can give him the same signal, maybe no more than a click of my fingers, and he'll do exactly the same thing.'

Scientific researchers who ask dolphins to collaborate in complex experiments have reached the same conclusion. They find their subjects attentive, lively, interested in everything. 'The speed at which dolphins learn,' says Dr Lilly, 'is comparable to that of humans.'

Frohn has persuaded his dolphins to jump fifteen feet in the air to ring a bell, snap a fresh mackerel or delicately pluck a cigarette from the corner of his mouth; he has made them swim backwards on their tails, jump through paper hoops or leave the water to crawl about on land, a most unnatural thing for them to do. For the amusement of humans he has taught them to play simple human games – bowling, basket-ball, deck tennis and so on, in which their skill and taste for acrobatics give them champion status.

At Sea World in San Diego, California, the dolphins perform a short morality play in partnership with four pretty mermaids. The first act is a graceful ballet about the innocence and beauty of Eden-under-the-Sea. The second act introduces a fisherman

140

of vandalistic propensities; in the third act the dolphins tidy up his refuse – beer cans and dirty wrappings; in the fourth, shamed by their behaviour, the wicked tourist realizes the error of his ways and is converted to love of, and respect for, nature.

At the Sea Life Park in Hawaii local girls in their *pareus* play a modern version of the story of Arion, and very few shows indeed have ever featured together such intelligent and such pretty mammals.

In all such places the only reward given during training is a fish, and the only punishment, no fish. And later, when the game has been understood and learnt, the mere pleasure of the thing is a sufficient incentive in itself. Dr Wood has seen a dolphin keep up a difficult role for a whole day – six shows in all – without receiving a single fish. 'You will never,' says Frohn, 'get anywhere with a dolphin by force. If you try it, he'll break off contact, retire to the farthest corner of the pool and ignore you. If you persist, he'll go on a hunger strike. He'll let himself die rather than submit to doing something against his will.'

One day at the Seaquarium I realized to what extent Frohn has earned the love of his dolphins. Conklin and I were making clumsy efforts to get acquainted with two dolphins who were convalescing in isolation in small separate tanks. They accepted our caresses, but with little more than a polite show of interest. They obliged us by posing for snapshots, obviously without enthusiasm. Suddenly, a radical transformation: both dolphins reared their bodies half way out of the water, quivered and squealed, their eyes fixed on the corner of a wall. For a good twenty seconds they stayed like that, all excited. They were waiting. But for what? Then Frohn appeared round the corner of the wall. They could not have seen him coming; they did not smell him, for they have no sense of smell; they did not detect him by sonar, which works only in water; and yet, long before we knew, they knew that the man they had learnt to love was on his way. And once he is on the scene, their enthusiasm is like that of children running to greet their father on his return home from work. And when Frohn speaks of his charges, of some illness or an operation which has kept him on watch beside one of them night and day, it is 'my little girl this' and 'my little boy that', and the words sound perfectly natural on his lips.

The importance of these marine circuses, then, is enormous and twofold: they enable the public to know the dolphins better and teach respect for them and for nature in general, and at the same time their scientific installations are always open to those in search of learning and provide laboratories of exceptional value.

Of course, shipborne zoologists had already established that Odontoceti are social animals. It was known that they move from place to place like an army, organized under a leader, sending scouts ahead to test suspect areas and deploying their crack units in a protective screen around the weaker members in the middle. Observations from land had shown how pilot whales would form up in the mornings towards their hunting-ground, disperse to feed, and regroup in the evenings before making their way back to where they came from. Witnesses had seen, in a water made red with blood, a pack of thirty Pacific killer whales circling a group of some hundred dolphins, penning them like Indians might a beleaguered wagon train, while one after another the whales would leave the formation to seize a dolphin, devour it and resume position, leaving the next whale its turn at killing.

But observations of this kind, made from a distance, did not usually permit a definite identification of the animals, nor did they indicate the precise motivations of their actions, their social habits and family life, or their methods of communication. Whereas today, watching through an observation window, or moving in the same medium as the animals themselves, cetologists can observe the object of their study in its life – its movements, its breathing, its games, its love-making. They watch the dolphins give birth to their young, suckle them, care for them, initiate them into the life of the group, care for the sick and die. And it is by watching them night and day, season after season, year after year that scientists have been able to amass the information we now possess about the social behaviour of the dolphin and about the personality and intelligence of individual animals.

In this way Margaret Tavolga was able, over a period of five years, to follow the life of a stable colony of captive *Tursiops truncati* comprising initially one male and four females plus, eventually, as many as eight offspring. She found here a clearly defined hierarchy. Certain individuals dominated by virtue of greater aggressiveness and lack of fear and could apparently, by bullying, impose their will on the others without ever being bullied themselves. The adult male led the rank-order; under him came the adult females, then the young males, and lastly the pups. The leading male, calm and peaceable, never used force unless provoked by, for example, a young male stealing a fish that he himself had his eye on, or showing too obtrusive an interest in his females. Generally a loud snap of the jaws sufficed to put the youngster to flight: should he persist, then a butt, a nip or a smash of the tail would hurl him against the side of the pool. After such a lesson the offender would keep himself to himself for several days. The leader swam alone most of the time or, in spring, with some of the females.

Among the females, too, there was a tireless leader whom others would follow in all the games she organized. Another female remained aloof, passive and reserved, living a calm and retired existence on her own.

The young males formed a separate sub-clan which, by its turbulence, often got entangled at the wrong time in the activities of its seniors. This group had its own chief, often something of a buffoon.

The very young stuck to their mothers' shadows for the first few months. Later they would become bolder and take little side-trips on their own to play with other infants, but up to one and a half years old they would still scurry for shelter under their mothers at the first sign of danger or in response to her call. They ate their first fish at four to six months, but continued to take the breast long after that. When they reach about eighteen months – or sooner if she becomes pregnant again – the mother will start pushing them away when they try to take the teat. (The period of gestation is nearly twelve months. Twins are exceptional.)

When a dolphin pup is born all the adults form a protective

circle to defend the mother, while incapacitated by her contractions, against the sharks, which are sometimes present in the pool and are attracted and excited by the thin cloud of blood. Margaret Tavolga has seen a mother helped during the birth of her first child by her own mother, who never left her for a moment during the final months of pregnancy, during the birth itself or during the first months of nursing. If there is no grandmother, each baby has, from the moment of its birth, a 'godmother' – another female who looks after him as if he were her own whenever the mother has to leave him in search of food or to play her part in the show. If the mother should die, adoption is automatic. Sometimes the godmother functions as a babysitter, looking after two or three infants at a time, a job which, of course, keeps her busy day and night.

Once they have become mothers, the females devote all their time to the care of their young. They steer the pups away from all new or unknown objects until the others, in close defensive formation and led by a scout (always the same daring young female) have been to investigate it visually and by sonar. They push their charges to the far end of the pool when adults start jumping or engage in rough play. The first few days the mother will lean on her side to let the baby reach the teat, but gradually the nurselings become more adept and learn to reach the teat from below without interfering with the mother's swimming. If he moves away from his mother, she brings him back; if he does it again, he gets a spanking – aquatic style: she either squeezes him against the bottom of the pool for thirty seconds, or alternatively holds him in her flippers out of the water for the same length of time. The games of love, unlike humans, they do not play in all seasons. Their love affairs are conducted with no less enthusiasm and imagination than ours, but often – as Conklin told me one day – with greater delicacy.

Roger Conklin, too, has spent days and days watching his beloved dolphins through the underwater portholes of the pool at Miami's Seaquarium. When he tells about them, he is both a poet and a naturalist in the great tradition of the Greeks.

'You should see them,' I remember him saying. 'When a male has first noticed a particular female he will follow her from a

144

distance and quite discreetly, then closer and closer. If he is not ignored or rebuffed he will begin a kind of seduction dance by flexing and posturing his sleek body as he glides, swirls and suddenly stops, forming himself in an S-curve before her, his head up and tail flukes down.

'If he receives encouragement, if the female also poses her body similarly, then a couple is formed which will live only with one another and for one another for days or weeks.

'As the two swim side by side, belly to belly with but inches separating them, each takes his or her turn in stroking the other with a feathery movement of the flippers across the belly. They tease each other and nuzzle or lightly bite each other's nose.

'With a fluke he titillates her white belly and her vulva. With her closed mouth she caresses his genital slit. Sometimes you will see the male dolphin pump his tail up and down at a furious pace to swim away, then turn sharply, and come back straight towards her. He will turn aside a fraction of a second before the collision and dash past her, vigorously rubbing the underside of her body with his own as he swooshes by. Then he may go away but if you look carefully you will see his blow-hole vibrating.

'He is calling her – and she will go and join him at the other end of the pool. Then he will be silent and they will both swim together again belly to belly and nuzzling and rubbing each other.

'Sometimes she acts the coquette and, swooshing away from him, soars to the surface and leaps into the sunshine. But as she plummets back into the sea, there he is, right at the place where she will re-enter the water and, as she flashes past him, their bodies will rub together again. Now both are aroused. She titillates and nuzzles and strokes his genital organ again and suddenly the lips of the opening part and his erected sex organ appears. She leans to him, very close; he and she are united and, one flesh and one body, they face their swimming movements, now smooth and unbroken, and as he thrusts his pelvis forward in short bursts to penetrate her deeper, their embraced figures playing out the drama of creation do look almost human.'

You see, I told you, Roger Conklin *is* a poet.

Dolphins occasionally practice homosexuality even when surrounded by complaisant females – so that, unlike in our prisons, pure necessity cannot be the cause. They also practise masturbation, rubbing themselves against whatever is available, and sodomy, which they attempt, generally without success, on rays, eels, sand-sharks or turtles. None of which prevents them from giving themselves up, an instant later, to the healthy pleasures of courtship and normal love, with a female dolphin or porpoise or with a member of a related species (male Atlantic *Tursiops* with female Pacific *Lagenorhynchus*, for example).

Modern psychologists place flexibility of behaviour and ready and effective adaptation to unforeseen circumstances among the criteria of intelligence which are the most general and the least subjective in their application. However, as the 'anti-dolphin's intelligence' party have never failed to point out, dolphins sometimes show a lack of flexibility which would appear irrational in man. They tell us, for instance, how in the open sea a mother dolphin will push a dead pup to the surface and hold him there for days and weeks. This is true; the ancient Greeks had remarked on it. It is also true that dolphins will even do the same with a piece of flotsam or the corpse of a baby shark. But, among humans, isn't it common for an old spinster to transfer to a pet dog her unused maternal instinct? And what is the first reaction of a human mother when she is told of the death of a beloved child? She will refuse to believe it. She will reject proof with all her force. And so we sometimes see a mother who suffers maybe from some psychological weakness endlessly rocking an empty cradle or continuing to nurse the lifeless body of her child. And if we normally describe this impassioned madness of a human mother by such terms as 'supreme love' and 'marvellous devotion', or in other cases 'sublime maternal sacrifice', why then should we call the same behaviour in a heartbroken dolphin mother another 'blind animal instinct'?

Describing the dolphin's behavioural rigidity, furthermore, is a two-edged weapon, and the other edge is the sharpest one by far. Since men have started to observe dolphins round the clock they have collected in their files a rich harvest of incidents which do prove the perfect adaptability of the dolphin's behaviour. Here are one or two, chosen from among hundreds, which illustrate these animals' capacity for reflection and their ability to apply the results of their quick thinking to the solution of a complex problem.

The first example was published in irreproachably impersonal, prudent and documented scientific idiom by Brown and Norris in the highly respectable *Journal of Mammalogy*. Here, translated from scientific jargon into English, is the actual sequence of events as observed by David Brown at Marineland of the Pacific, where he is curator of mammals. A dolphin:

1. selected a moray eel, apparently, as a new play-partner;
2. tried in vain to dislodge it from its hole between two rocks by pulling with his teeth at the end of its tail, which was sticking out, while another dolphin, recruited to help, tried to frighten it at the other end of the hole;
3. took a few moments' break on the surface, possibly for reflection;
4. killed a poison-spined scorpion fish with a blow of his beak in the belly (the only undefended area of the fish's body);
5. took the fish in his mouth holding it gingerly by the belly;
6. stung the eel's tail with the scorpion fish's spines;
7. dropped the fish and rushed to seize the eel which was making a bolt for open water;
8. played with the eel, throwing it out of the water and catching it again until he became, as it seemed, tired of the game;
9. let the eel go.

In other words, we seem justified in concluding that the dolphin, which eats neither eels nor venomous fishes, *invented* a technique to solve his problem of the moment with the available means. First he enlisted the aid of an assistant, then thought of a ruse which involved by-passing a defence mechanism and turning it into an effective tool – and all this for the mere pleasure of playing a game!

What might the dolphin not be capable of then, if its very life was at stake? Or if one were to vary the nature of the problem, at the same time increasing the number of tools at his disposal?

Well, that is exactly what we are about to find out, for our other examples of reasoning and behaving in a concerted, adequate and effective way have to do with the ways in which all cetaceans help one another in case of serious danger.

The basic first-aid technique consists of supporting on the surface a wounded or unconscious member of the group to enable him to breathe. A single dolphin, if there is only one around, will support the injured one from beneath; if there are two, each puts one flipper under a flipper of the wounded and will continue to hold him afloat for days at a time if necessary, working a shift system, if numbers permit, in relays of two. This system has been observed in operation hundreds of times among all species of cetaceans. They will do it not only for their own kind, but even for members of different species from different oceans, who happen to be present in the same pool. For this reason, when an aquarium has a sick dolphin on its hands, caring for its physical and moral well-being is now largely left to other dolphins, as vitamins and antibiotics alone cannot do the job.

Among dolphins medical practice is not the blind hit-or-miss affair that it is among our own witch-doctors with their all-purpose poultices, or among yesterday's graduated doctors who systematically prescribed the twin cure-alls of cupping and bleeding. Dr Lilly had once kept a dolphin almost immobile for several days in a tailor-made small tank in the course of some experiment. The animal was in water but unable to move. Cold and inactivity had stiffened the nerves and muscles of the dolphin's tail to the point where they refused to respond to commands. Lilly failed to notice this when he returned him to the main tank. Half paralysed, the sinking animal immediately put out a Dolphinese SOS. Immediately two others rallied to its side and lifted its head out of the water so that it could breathe. It took one breath and sank. Then the hydrophones transmitted to Lilly a quick exchange of whistles. After a few moments of this 'discussion' the rescue team made a complete change of tactics: instead of holding their companion's head out of the water, they began swimming beneath him at regular intervals in such a way that with each passage their dorsal fins would stroke his anal region; the stimulus to this sensitive area caused a reflex contraction of the stiffened muscles which forced down the tail fin and thus at the same time pushed the head clear of the water. The two rescuers by turns continued this strange artificial respiration for several hours.

Thus the initial distress call brought an emergency first-aid type response. The immediate crisis over, the incapacitated dolphin explained the situation and the others then applied a specific treatment, obviously known to them, as it was put into effect at once with no trial and error.

Lilly, again, at the Washington Symposium mentioned another extraordinary example of Dolphinese therapy.

A dolphin pup, bottle fed on a synthetic milk which was over-rich in lactose, was suffering so badly from wind that it was unable to swim upright. The gas in its swollen intestines was causing it to float belly up. Its struggle to straighten itself was exhausting it. At this point an adult male approached and by thrusting its muzzle hard against the pup's belly succeeded in expelling the gases through the natural orifice.

William Evans reports another case:

A sick young female dolphin would repeatedly interrupt her echo-sounding emissions. Disoriented, she would smash against the concrete walls of the pool and tear her skin off. Each time, another female would drop whatever she was doing and dash to her side to interpose her own body between the side of the tank and the sick companion and she would stay with her until she was sure that the crisis had passed. The condition of the young female deteriorated, but during the 48 hours her agony lasted, every time she sank or thrashed about confusedly, she was borne up again to the surface by her companion.

So really, if the dolphin-doctor can question his patient, discuss the case with him and his fellow physicians, make a diagnosis, apply, or cause to be applied, a specific treatment which is prolonged until a cure is achieved, has he not crossed the borderline between instinctive behaviour – by definition both immutable and unreasoning – and intelligent behaviour? And does this not perhaps explain why Lilly's work is funded by the National Institute of Health, the Public Health Service and the National Institute for Blindness and Neurological Diseases?

Direct observation has taught us also that dolphins do not live by fish alone. Without a reason for living, dolphins will refuse to live. In captivity they need action and games, they need variety. They will not react day after day like trained rats to mechanical stimuli by conditioned-reflex responses. If they are asked too often to do the same simple trick they grow bored and either cease to collaborate or else shower their tormentor with a well-aimed tail stroke, as Dr Norris often found out at the University of California.

Being sociable animals, they cannot stand solitude. Left alone, a captive dolphin finds it dull and stops feeding. He actually pines away to the point where he may die. But bring him a companion, stimulate his interest, give him something exciting to do, and he comes to life again. The story of Pauline, as told by Brown and Norris, is an example. Pauline, a young female recently captured and injured, arrived in the tank in a state of shock. In spite of adrenalin injections she remained listless and let herself sink as soon as left to herself. Brown attached four buoys to her body to keep her on the surface. She floated like this for three days, indifferent to everything, refusing to move or to take any food. Then Brown introduced a companion into the tank. The male immediately approached her. Did he speak to her? She immediately reacted, moved, tried to swim. Her buoys were removed and she began, stiffly and painfully, to swim, while the male gave her an occasional push towards the surface. Thanks to his help she recovered completely. They became inseparable. Two months later she died of a long-term complication of the injury she had received at the time of her capture. The male lamented her death with continuous whistling. He circled endlessly around the lifeless body and from that day refused all food. For three days his lamentations could be heard. For three days he continued to swim in a hopeless circle, and at the end of the third day he died. Autopsies have never been performed on romantic lovers who have died of 'heartbreak', but Brown and Norris report that the autopsy they performed in this case 'revealed the presence of a perforated gastric ulcer'. They add: 'The ulcer was probably aggravated by the animal's refusal to eat thus causing the perforation, the peritonitis to which this gave rise, and death. Healed gastric ulcers have since been found in two other subjects examined in our laboratories. The prime cause of these ulcers has not been determined.'

'Frustrated sexual instinct,' you may say. Very well, but then it was also from a frustration of their sexual instinct that Romeo and Juliet died at the foot of their social obstacle, and that, really, was not worth the fuss that men made about it in literature.

Not only do they know passionate love founded on sex, but dolphins also show friendship, a pure spiritual affection whose pleasures lie only in the joys of companionship. At Marineland of California there once were two friendly males who lived in perfect harmony in a pool which they shared with a number of females. One of them was taken from the pool to star in a series of shows elsewhere. Three weeks later he was brought back. The two friends' display of joy was truly explosive. For hours they swam about together excitedly and leapt together high out of the water. For days after they remained inseparable, and ignored their consorts completely. 'Old acquaintance' is not valued by humans alone.

Platonic affection is not confined either to relationships between dolphins. To Pliny we owe the famous account of the friendship of the child of Baiae with the dolphin Simo (see page 20).

At Iasos, on the Island of Porosolene, both Oppian and Pausanias witnessed a similar friendship which ended tragically. 'When death had taken the child ... the dolphin refused the food the local fishermen offered him ... and finally was seen no more. ... Without any doubt it was the loss of his departed friend which killed him' (Oppian, *Halieutica*).

It was the easier for the Greeks not to doubt this since they also knew that 'Dolphins, at one time, were men, and in their conscious souls they retain the memory of it.' And for proof they would point to the friendly feelings dolphins still have towards mankind. A man, as well as another dolphin, can relieve the grief of a dolphin's loneliness. At Pickering Zoo, in England, in 1965, a mother dolphin who had lost her baby was letting herself die of hunger. A psychiatrist and a nurse, in diving dress, went into the water every day to spend long hours with her. They succeeded in restoring her will to live. At the Oceanography Museum in Monaco, French researchers had a similar experience: their dolphin would consent to keep alive only if continuously amused and cared for. To economize on effort all marine circuses now put a quiet and sociable tame dolphin in with each newcomer. The old hand shows the new one the ropes and, perhaps, relieves his early misery. At Niagara Falls Aquarium they found that Florida dolphins did not get on at all well. They were so depressed that the shows could not go on. Vitamins were tried with other therapies, but finally doctors and psychiatrists had to face the facts: the dolphins who were living there shut away indoors were homesick for their own sun and blue waters. For fear of losing them they were flown back to Florida for holiday and rest cure.

To renounce life for the sake of something which one holds to be more important than life itself is to overcome the primeval instinct of self-preservation, and is this not yet another criterion of intellectual development? A criterion, also, which human beings have always believed proper only to them, whether disgraced samurai, prisoners who know too much, desperate lovers, neurotics or ruined financiers?

Nor is this all. Men who still look at themselves as the ornament of creation have some illusions to lose. For example, overworked company directors might like to know that ulcers and coronaries, the mark of the élite, the glorious stigmata of devotion to the firm, also occur in dolphins. At the Marine Sciences Division of the Naval Missile Center (California) a Dall dolphin died of a stomach haemorrhage which doctors attributed to tension induced by captivity. In the Soviet Union, Dr Yablokov and his assistant, Ivan Belkovitch, while performing autopsies on dead dolphins, have found to their amazement that some of them 'had died from heart attacks or cerebral thromboses'.

Well then, if dolphins can suffer from illnesses caused by worries, mental strain, spiritual suffering or intellectual overwork, does not it prove to some that they, too, possess the intelligence that kills?

Just as men play – throwing and catching balls or gliding on skis, purely for the fun of it – so do cetaceans play by throwing anything handy into the air. At sea dolphins, and even sperm whales, will play with anything they find floating, tortoises, wreckage, driftwood, coconuts. One day at Marineland a fine selection of tropical fish was put into the main pool. The dolphins immediately began to throw them to the spectators; they did it delicately and with great precision. When they are given a ball or a hoop they organize a game among themselves just for sport.

At the Marine Studio, where the upkeep of the pool is done by divers, there are two fashionable sports among young male dolphins. The rules of one game go like this: you sneak up on the diver from behind, you wind his air hose round a flipper or your tail, then you take off. The diver is hauled over backwards and, if you are quick enough, may even lose his helmet. It is marvellous fun. The other game can be played only when a diver comes to rake the sand at the bottom of the tank. The end of the rake always sticks out under his arm. You take it in your teeth, you pull, and you have him.

There are also team games. Players position themselves at either end of a tunnel of rocks and chase the fish hiding there from one end to another. Or one will take a pelican feather and place it on the underwater jet which feeds the pool. The feather is whirled up to the surface where it is caught by a second player, who takes it back to the jet and takes his place there while the first player has his turn as the catcher.

We are proud enough of our famous 'leisured society', available to so few until so recently, and so ill enjoyed by most. The Odontoceti are a 'success' in life far more than we are. They are better organized than we, have been so for ages, spend as much time in play as we in work, and as little time in working to live as we in playing.

We fancy ourselves to be experts in frustration, cast as we are upon an inhospitable world. Here, then, is food for meditation: a feeling of frustration presupposes a judgement, and a hostile one at that, of a given situation. A woman may break a vase in anger, a man may hammer on a table with his fist, and a dolphin, too, can experience the need to break something in a moment of frustration. During a series of visual discrimination tests, a *Tursiops* called Paddy, who was working with Kellog and Rice, would show clear signs of frustration every time he made the wrong choice and received no reward. The reward consisted of no more than a tiny piece of fish and Paddy was already more than adequately fed, so it is reasonable to suppose that his frustration stemmed not from hunger but from the conscious realization of his failure. One day, exasperated by a succession of mistakes – which by the way, were partly the fault of the experimenters, Paddy sank his teeth into a length of plastic tube which was lying around on the bottom and demolished the whole experimental apparatus with a succession of furious blows.

Surely, after so many specific objective and detailed examples, you will now have formed your own opinion about the intelligence of the dolphin. We may draw some conclusions, based on the most astonishing and moving of these examples, as to the 'moral qualities' of the dolphin. The point is of importance if we wish to extend legal protection to the dolphin as has been done in New Zealand and the U.S.S.R. Cuvier provides some support: 'We believe that the dolphin is a highly intelligent animal, endowed with valuable moral qualities.' But since Cuvier's time, Darwin and other researchers on the mechanism of evolution have demonstrated that, in species where intelligence is a factor of survival – and only in those species – it develops in the same manner as any other physical characteristic that has survival value. (Earthworms manage very well without any intelligence to speak of.) In this area both dolphin and man, since the far distant epoch when both began to diverge from a common ancestor, have evolved according to the same mechanism.

As Sir Gavin de Beer has pointed out, we are led to call 'fine' and 'good' those forms of conduct which have helped us (men or animals) to survive in a hostile environment. 'In many of the higher animals,' he explains in his *Handbook on Evolution,* parental care and self-sacrifice in the interest of other members of the family such as incubating or pregnant females and young, have been favoured by natural selection and conferred benefit on the species.'

Can one not add that in the course of our history altruistic actions have spread beyond the bounds of the family to the tribe, to the nation, and recently to humanity as a whole, and that it is as a parallel development that behavioural patterns which favoured the survival of these larger groups have been set up as examples and have become – with the aid of such supports as education, law, religion and social pressure – the basis of our morality?

I should like to quote de Beer one last time: 'With the development of man's higher mental faculties, the pooling of experience by speech-communication, and its storage in memory, conscious choice and purposiveness became factors in evolution. Hence its subsequent psycho-social evolution has been of a nature different from that of other organisms, because it was no longer governed solely by natural selection and therefore involved processes outside the scope of natural selection.'

Where is all this leading us? The conclusion is pretty obvious. The toothed whales have a language, an excellent memory, they make conscious choices and they have given frequent proofs of goal-oriented behaviour. For a period of time infinitely longer than man's, their psycho-social evolution has been of a different nature, too, from that of other animals. But 'of a different nature' does not necessarily mean 'of a nature similar to that of humans'.

Let us give the last word to Professor Yablokov on behalf of Soviet researchers. Though we know little of the details of their work, here are the reflections which fifteen years of research inspired in him:

155

There is considerable evidence to support the view that the dolphins are radically different from other members of the animal world. The question arises, 'What is the dolphin?' And what is his relationship to Man, that supreme form of matter, matter which – to rephrase Engels – has become conscious of itself?

It is possible that matter has made, at one stage or another in its endless evolution, other attempts at self-knowledge, which have been to some extent successful. Man represents one of such attempts, probably the most successful.

It is not only isolated organisms which evolve, but rather large groups of homogeneous species, and human society is the most highly complex group that we know of. But that of the dolphins too, is extraordinarily complex. Suffice it to say that up to ten generations coexist at one time in dolphin societies. If that were the case with man, Leonardo da Vinci, Lomonoscov, Faraday and Einstein would still be alive. ... Could not the dolphin's brain contain an amount of information comparable in volume to the thousands of tons of books in our libraries? Whatever our opinion of the dolphin, it will not be more than a human judgement due to the limitations of our knowledge.

'The less intelligent the white man, the more stupid he finds the black'; so André Gide wrote in his *Journey to the Congo*. Isn't this equally true of all those who use their own means and goals as a criterion to measure an intelligence other than their own which another man, or a dolphin, applies in other ways, to other goals in a different context?

The Aquanaut's Companion

When the new Stone Age dawned and our ancestors passed out of the food-gathering and hunting stages, settled down and began to practise agriculture and crop husbandry, they formed a permanent association with certain animals that were useful to them. Without the horse, the goat, the llama, the reindeer, the camel, their life would have been much harder, as it would have been harder for hunters and fishermen without the dog, the falcon and the cormorant.

Today, in what is the prehistory of submarine man, divers are about to pass out of the hunting stage and the food-gathering stage and to begin farming the Continental Shelf. The plundering raids will give way to long periods of productive occupation by settlers. But in what will still be a hostile environment, it seems to me that tomorrow's farmers of the sea-bed would do well to seek out allies.

These allies, as in the time of Arion, will be dolphins and porpoises, as well as the great toothed whales, seals, sea-lions, and perhaps also their cumbersome cousins, the walruses and elephant seals.

A Utopian idea? Not at all. Mutual understanding is possible without speech, and in some degree truth has already outstripped fiction. A special unit of the U.S. Navy has been exploring all the possibilities of collaboration between man and marine mammals since 1964, and the aquanauts of *Sealab II* had completed their team with a certain 'Tuffy', who was in fact a *Tursiops* dolphin. *Sealab II* is the second of the 'Houses under the Sea' which Dr Bond, father of the project, got the U.S. Navy to set up in 1965, some thirty fathoms down off La Jolla, California. Tuffy was so called from evidence of toughness visible in the many scars on his sides, no doubt relics of many duels with sharks; for although the dolphin, faster and more cunning than the shark, can dodge its terrible teeth it cannot always avoid contact with the shark's skin, the effect of which on its own delicate hide is like a rasp on satin.

Before starting on a specialized course to qualify him for certain jobs as an assistant aquanaut, Tuffy, six feet five overall and weighing three hundred pounds, had spent more than eighteen months in a special pond at the Marine Biology Center in the Division of Marine Science of the Naval Missile Center at Point Mugu, California. Forrest G. Wood, Director of the Center, and his assistant Sam Ridgeway, a veterinary surgeon, have the task of finding by experiment what degree of confidence men can place in certain marine mammals when tamed and trained to help them in their work.

Tuffy had got used to wearing a special harness to which could be fixed objects or instruments, and had been trained to respond to certain sound signals by coming to the source of sound immediately. He had shown himself enthusiastic and interested while in the pond, and perfectly trustworthy in the open sea. He had done countless dives out in the ocean, sometimes as deep as forty-five fathoms, and he reacted to call signals at a range up to five hundred yards. So that when Dr Bond undertook his second experiment in saturation diving, he was from the first making an unprecedented experiment in mustering a toothed whale among the crew of *Sealab II*.

In September 1965, after five weeks of special training and some days spent in getting to know the two aquanauts with whom he was going to work on the sea bed, Tuffy, lying on a stretcher and wrapped in a wet blanket, made the trip from Point Mugu to La Jolla in a helicopter. There he took up his quarters in a floating cage alongside the supply ship *Berkone* and was to emerge from it many times in the following week to fulfil his different tasks.

For the first few days he seemed confused and perhaps

frightened by the complicated network of cables, electric wires and ropes that ran in all directions, by the submerged lights and above all by the din, the snoring of engines, by the crashing and banging which emanated from the steel submarine house and from the supply ship and the barges. For a creature with such delicate hearing all this must have sounded like a sheet metal workshop operating full bore, but once he had got used to it he became once more the trustworthy fellow worker he had been before.

The chief danger for an aquanaut working outside his submarine dwelling or laboratory is that of getting lost; if he loses his guide line, or loses sight of the lights, if the current bears him away, or rising mud troubles the waters, he is done for. The situation is all the worse since he cannot even try to come up to the surface, where an immediate and frightfully painful death from the 'bends' would await him. Could a dolphin on the bottom play the part of a St Bernard dog and bring the lost diver to safety? This was the question to be answered by experiment.

So on the sixth day one of the aquanauts wandered away from *Sealab*, as if lost, setting off the sound device which he wore on his wrist and to which Tuffy had been trained to react. But before responding to it, Tuffy knew he must first respond to another, alarm bell No. 1, emanating from the rescue diver. Tuffy, wearing his harness, was swimming freely about the ocean when he heard both signals. Immediately he dived towards the rescue man (at not less than thirty-one fathoms), who fixed a line to his harness. Then he darted off just as quickly, unreeling the line towards the 'lost' diver, whom he picked up on his sonar some sixty yards away and reached in a few seconds. He waited until the lost man could detach and grasp the line that would lead him to safety. Then he calmly surfaced.

On that day the operation went off three times running without a hitch. Each time, one minute ten seconds after the alarm, Tuffy was back on the surface, mission accomplished.

Of course the system can be simplified: the lost diver calls the dolphin, who comes down, carrying a ring to which a line is permanently attached and gives it to the lost man; or else, more simply still, the dolphin goes in search of the lost man, who takes hold of the harness and is towed towards the laboratory.

The following days Tuffy's work was more routine: humdrum daily tasks, odd jobs as porter or errand-boy. At a signal he brought the diver messages and outgoing mail from the underwater house. Punctual and efficient, the dolphin would do seven return trips in less time than it would have taken a diver to put on his diving suit and gear.

When Tuffy had completed all his tasks and gone home, a psychologist attached to the Navy's Submarine Medicine Center, Mike Greenwood, noticed that six sea-lions were frequenting the waters around the *Berkone*. The men below had seen them occasionally peering in at the portholes, or feasting on the abundance of fish attracted by the clouds of plankton dancing in the rays of the submerged lights. Greenwood wanted to try out on them the training techniques which had succeeded so well with Tuffy. He set off the same kind of underwater electric alarm clock that had served to summon the dolphin. At the first ring the most inquisitive of the sea-lions, which was over two hundred yards off, came to see what it was all about. From then onwards, for a solid month, Sam, as he was named having been rewarded with a mackerel the first time, never missed his mackerel (or her, for in spite of the opinion of those who did the christening, a dissenting minority maintained that Samantha would be a more fitting name). In one day he responded thirty times to thirty summonses. He even learned to jump six feet out of the water if that was where the reward was presented. But Sam never let anyone come near him. When divers were in the water he prudently kept his distance, and out of six sea-lions in the area, four flatly refused to play with men.

Then Greenwood sent down the signal device to the aquanauts and asked them to call up the animal themselves. After every ring they saw, framed in the watery circle of their entry hatch, a little round head with moustached muzzle and black inquisitive eyes; it was a moving and also rather frightening sight, because when a diver comes up from thirty fathoms after breathing in, he has seven times the normal content of gas in his lungs. If he does not breathe out continually as he comes up, pulmonary over-pressure will give him a fatal embolism, the expanding gas passing in bubbles into his blood through the walls of the alveoli. Happily, anxiety was dispelled at once: the sea-lion was seen to breathe out very calmly, through the nostrils, expelling all the air stored in the lungs as it came up.

However, there remains another problem which must be kept in mind in the future: if a marine mammal which is normally a breath-holding diver breathes compressed air under the surface for too long (which at thirty fathoms means for a few minutes), or worse still breathes a mixture of gases artificially compounded, it will suffer from decompression sickness on surfacing, as Scholander's experiments with seals in a hyperbaric chamber have shown.

But it was at the end of the experiment that Sam was to give the clearest proof of his intelligence. Dr Greenwood tried all possible means to catch the sea-lion for dispatch to Point Mugu and training there, but he eluded all traps, avoided all nets, and at this very hour he is still enjoying life, freedom and the pursuit of happiness off the coast of California.

What the good and faithful services of Tuffy have proved is that even if we have not arrived at the stage of dialogue with dolphins, these old marine hands will be more valuable than the most sophisticated robots to the human aquanaut, that newcomer among the aquatic mammals. For the next experiment, *Sealab II*, two dolphins, two sea-lions and a seal will be mustered among the crew.

The marine mammals will not be mere errand-boys. Under the sea man is a Babe in the Woods, a disoriented Tom Thumb, short-sighted at best and often blind. The tame dolphin will be his seeing-eye dog, to take him to work and home again. He will be his bodyguard, his cheetah, his falcon, keeping his table supplied with fresh fish and lobsters. The noblest conquest of *homo aquaticus*, he will be his mount, as was the horse in antiquity, but a steed faster than any submarine vehicle and with no batteries to run down.

161

Under water man is unable to move loads. Cetaceans will become his draught and pack animals. Recent experiments a Point Mugu have shown that a harnessed dolphin can tow three times its own weight under water. The porpoise, at about 17½ lb. or 220 lb., can shift more than six hundredweight. It will be the husky dog of submarine expeditions. Dolphins of all species at twice this weight, will draw over half a ton, like cart-horses The Beluga, the white whale of the polar seas, will be the equivalent of a pair of reindeer, towing more than a ton. Perhaps the killer whale, which weighs more than six tons, or the midge sperm, or at least the pilot whale, will be the water buffaloes of the ocean. As for the sperm whale itself, its fifty tons times three will give it the tractive capacity of a team of elephants.

The black pilot whale is a familiar sight to us now, and many American aquaria have pairs of them in captivity. They are superb slender beasts with rounded heads and impressive teeth The males measure up to eighteen feet, the females twelve or fifteen. In the presence of man they are very sociable, even though, now and again, through nervousness or clumsiness the jostle a diver about. David Brown, who has had a lot to do with them in the big tank at the Marineland of California, calls thei capacity for learning 'altogether remarkable'. He adds: 'The pilot whale's capacity for adjustment to captivity and it favourable response to training immediately after capture are even more remarkable than the behaviour of captive dolphins whether *Tursiops* common or striped. We may doubt whether the pilot whale is the most intelligent of the three species, but certainly it is the one which has the least fear of contact with man.'

The killer whale is another thing altogether.

Certainly it is the most splendid, the most fascinating perhaps the most diabolically clever of all animals. Its scientific name *Orcinus orca* replaces an earlier, more dramatic term *Orca gladiator*. While its body weight is that of an elephant, it brain weighs seven times as much as an elephant's. Six to ten tons of streamlined muscle, it is glistening black on the back with a snow-white belly and broad white patches behind the head and on the back aft of the sharp triangular dorsal fin.

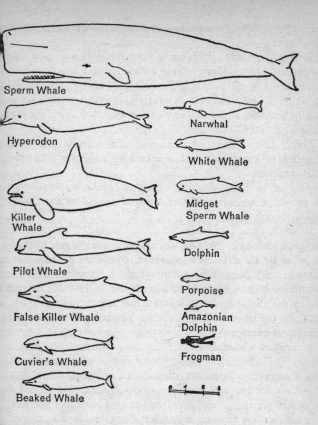

Sperm Whale

Hyperodon

Narwhal

White Whale

Killer Whale

Midget Sperm Whale

Pilot Whale

Dolphin

False Killer Whale

Porpoise

Amazonian Dolphin

Cuvier's Whale

Frogman

Beaked Whale

Fig. 10. Man and his cousins. Scale in metres. (After T. J. Walker.)

Orca is the king of the seas, fearing nobody and nothing. He has no enemies. His maw is enormous and terrifying, a chasm paved at the rim with a double row of sharp teeth slanting inwards, each the size of half a banana. No doubt on account of its impressive teeth it has enjoyed among men in all ages the reputation of a wolf, of an ogre of the seas.

Pliny the Elder: 'The killer whale cannot be properly depicted or described except as a great mass of flesh armed with cruel teeth.'

The Diving Manual of the United States Navy: 'The killer whale has a reputation of being a ruthless and ferocious beast. It is found in all oceans and seas.... Killer whales hunt in packs of 3 to 40 individuals preying on other warm blooded marine animals.... If a killer whale is seen in the area the diver should get out of the water immediately.'

Owen Lee, author of a monumental treatise on diving: 'There is no remedy against an attack by a killer whale, except Reincarnation.'

And yet no killer whale has ever, anywhere, killed, snapped at, mouthed, wounded, jostled, brushed against or even looked crossly at a human being.

Whence, then, this concerted cry of horror? First of all, because of its looks. When an animal looks dangerous, or might, to judge by its physical appearance, constitute a danger, it is automatically dubbed 'bloodthirsty' and 'a ferocious killer'. Let the fiction writers get hold of it, and swiftly the fable becomes reality for all the ignorant, which is as much as to say, in things touching the sea, for all landlubbers. The octopus of Giliatt is a significant example!

It must be added, however, that the celebrated post-mortem report by Dr Eschricht has done nothing to allay anxiety. One day Eschricht opened the stomach of an adult killer whale about twenty-two feet long; the stomach measured six feet by three feet six inches and contained several seals and porpoises and the remains of a larger number. Another stomach, that of a killer whale from the Bering Sea, contained thirty-two seals. Others contained only squids.

The stories of Tasmanian, Australian and other whalers who have seen packs of killer whales attacking right whales to eat their tongues and fins are no more reassuring. And they are probably true.

The dramatic account by Herbert Ponting has not helped, especially as it has been countless times repeated. Ponting was the photographer attached to Captain Scott's last Arctic expedition. He swore that he with his own eyes saw killer whales rocking ice floes by striking them with their tails, so as to tip off the seals who were sleeping on them. Once in the water the seals were done for. He even said that the killer whales had tried the same tactic against his sledge-dogs, without success, and finally against himself.

How much remains today of this reputation, now that the fears of yesteryear are confronted with the facts, now that man and killer whale live together? Well, very little.

Quite recently five killer whales were caught alive and lived long enough to be closely observed.

A bull *Orcinus,* wrongly named Moby Doll, spent eighty-five days in 1964 in a floating pen in the port of Vancouver. He proved to be a gentle, sociable animal, calm and instantly tame-able, eating out of the hand of Dr Newman, director of the local aquarium.

Another bull, twenty-two feet long, caught in June 1965 by salmon fishers in British Columbia, lived for a long time in a floating cage at Seattle. Ted Griffin, director of the public aquarium at Seattle, and other divers, had formed the habit of spending several hours a day in the water with Namu, stroking him, hand-feeding him under water and even riding him as Taras did his dolphin. When the water was muddy, all of them by accident put either a foot or hand in his mouth. The whale never once closed his jaws. William High, one of the diving photographers who thus approached him, has sent me close-ups of his teeth which are very impressive.

Sneezy, caught by Tony McLeod and Doug Muir, now lives in a pond at Stanley Park, Vancouver. He is twenty-five feet long. At San Diego's Marineland there is Shamu, a young killer whale weighing a mere ton and a half, who plays the game of Arion and the dolphin with his friends Tek Yuan (a Hawaiian) and Jim Richards. Apart from the riding act, the highlight of their number is when Tek Yuan puts his head far into the open mouth of the killer whale. And Orky at Marineland of the Pacific is just as tame as all the others.

But then these killers were isolated, hand-fed, tamed. Would I be prepared to dive into the sea and stroke a family of free-swimming killers if I were to meet one? To that question I have been postponing the answer for a long time.

Orky and Sneezy, the friends of man, are also, in captivity,

the friends of the dolphins who share their pond. But in the se
free-swimming killer whales swallow dolphins by the dozen.

As to the feeling of the sperm whales towards aquanaut
whether sociable or hostile, it would be vain to speculate, fo
we know nothing about them.

And here another problem suggests itself. How on eart
would one feed a tame sperm whale? Or a killer whale, which i
captivity may decide to touch nothing but fresh salmon? Woul
it be necessary to set them to work at fixed times, letting ther
forage for themselves outside working hours? But then, whe
would be the incentive to work? For what wages? Especiall
where there is no common language. Above all, when there ha
been so much bad blood between the species (exclusivel
whales' blood, of course).

If you find all this incredible or too far-fetched, think twic
It is neither more nor less so, I think, than any forecasts tha
might have been made twenty-five years ago about do
phins becoming circus performers and film stars, or playing th
part of St Bernard dogs to equally improbable sea-botto
dwellers.

Unfortunately it has been the professional war-makers wh
have taken these predictions most seriously and instantly a
plied them with enthusiasm to their fighting ends. Certain Am
erican naval officers are now talking of training dolphins to ki
hostile frogmen, as police dogs are taught to attack prowlers
the sound of a whistle. Captain Bond himself has suggested tha
friendly divers should be equipped with an individual soun
signal; hostile divers who did not possess this characteristic con
tinuous signal would be torn to shreds at sight, or rather
sound!

There is worse yet to come. Earthmen, since ancient time
have taught dogs to kill, horses to kill, elephants to kill. The
have used them as they use objects, detail them as 'Banza
volunteers, doomed to death. During the Second World W.
the Russians had trained dogs loaded with explosives to ru
under enemy tanks where an antenna activated a detonator ar
blew up both tank and dog. In the United States the Army ha
trained bats to carry incendiary charges with delay fuses. T

idea was to parachute them at night over strategic enemy installations, so that when, following their custom, they went to rest at dawn under the eaves, the phosphorus would start a fire. The project was abandoned when the *kamikaze* bats escaped from their keepers and set fire to the training barracks.

Will men carry their murderous madness under the waves?

Dr Rehman, of the U.S. Navy's Ordnance Experimental Station, at China Lake, California, writes:

> If communication between dolphin and man could be established and the animal proved trustworthy, then they could be employed as guides to divers or to carry mechanical devices (*sic*) up to interesting (*sic*) submerged objects, to place mines in American and foreign harbors or on shipping lanes, or even to report by radio the presence and bearing of submarines on the high seas.

All very well. But how will these prescient men of war justify the millions of dollars swallowed up by cetological research if the dolphins, having learned how to talk to men, turn out to be pacifists, as might well befit such intelligent creatures, or even (perish the thought) hardened Communists?

It is the misfortune of all scientific progress to further – especially at the outset – the aims of organized murder. But let us forget that. Instead let us give some thought to what cetaceans can do, in particular, to lighten the efforts of men peacefully engaged on the ocean floor. For today's aquanauts who live on the Continental Shelf for six weeks at a time are only pioneers in the very first outposts. They are there to mark the way for tomorrow's toilers of the sea who will come to plough and harrow and reap the ocean harvest.

The sea-bed, as has often been said, is virgin soil, two and a half times the area of our dry land surface. At present a narrow strip of it is accessible and exploitable: the shallow zone, from zero to a thousand feet deep, which we call the Continental Shelf. There men can live and work in safety, as three recent experiments have proved. (They are the MAN IN SEA project by Link and Stenuit, first and so far deepest, the SEALAB project by Dr Bond and the U.S. Navy, and CONSHELF by Cousteau and the O.F.R.S.)

167

We are also too well aware that in our overcrowded world, two thirds of whose people suffer from malnutrition, we must at all costs find fresh natural resources. Of food, first of all, but also of raw materials and energy. The ocean contains potentially more human foodstuff than the current world population of 3,000,000,000 could consume; more than they will need in 1978, when there will be 4,000,000,000; and even in A.D. 2000 when there may well be 6,000,000,000 human beings standing shoulder to shoulder on dry land, there will still be enough in the sea to feed them all.

It will be the task of the aquanauts to develop on the Continental Shelf the techniques of scientific cultivation, or rationalized fish breeding, of submarine mining and the production of fuel.

To cultivate the ocean crops, the vitamin-rich seaweeds and marine plants which the Japanese and all coastal dwellers of the Pacific have always eaten (and from which algine is extracted), the 'briny-boots' of the future, just like the 'mucky-boots' of above, will need machines or else animals; draught animals, pack animals, watch-dogs, and what not. But when submarine methods of agriculture have been fully worked out, when the right selection has been made out of some two thousand species of seaweed, from which to produce the marine 'wheat', 'potatoes', 'cabbage', oceanic 'pears', 'grapes' and 'cocoa', thieves will have to be scared off the plantations. We must keep the dolphin in mind as a watch-dog for this purpose.

There are two possible solutions to the problem of getting the sea to yield the billions of tons of protein that it contains in the form of fish, crustaceans and molluscs, instead of the beggarly 45,000,000 tons which is all that the fishermen in the world can catch every year – hardly $1\frac{1}{2}$ per cent of all human food consumption. The first would be equivalent to the transition from the Old to the New Stone Age. A maximum industrialization of fishing technique, leading to the most rapid and complete extermination of all edible piscine species. By this truly 'modern' means the Continental Shelf would be transformed into a desert in the space of a few years. The second solution is to husband our marine resources as we should have done our terrestrial ones, and to replace what we destroy. This is the way of rationalized breeding – the rearing on the one hand of the better quality species for direct consumption and on the other hand coarser varieties which are prolific breeders and quick-growing, to be fattened as rapidly as possible and made into fish-flour, the most economical concentrated protein that exists.

At Lowestoft Fishery Laboratory in England plaice-raising is being thus studied, and at Port Erin in the Isle of Man the White Fish Authority is manuring a vast bed of seaweed with nitrates on which a million fish a year will be pastured.

Researchers at the Marine Biological Laboratory of Helsingor in Denmark are busy in certain parts of the Baltic selecting species with high potential (the future poultry, pigs, cattle of the sea) and controlling the vermin (starfish, etc.). Also in furthering the growth of plankton, which is the starting-point of the whole animal food chain.

But come the day when the 'fish boys' of the deep, or even of the offshore shallows, set up in business, they may well need the equivalent of a cowboy's horse or a sheep-dog, to watch over their clawed, shelled or finned cattle.

The toothed whales may not object to lending a flipper to those other toilers of the sea, the miners and quarrymen who work on the sea-bed extracting such minerals as iron (Japan), diamond-bearing sands (South Africa), tin sands (Indonesia), gold-bearing sands (Alaska) or just plain stone, such as the *Steinfischer* of Pomerania who raise moraine boulders from the bottom of the Baltic for building material. Offshore oil divers, marine archaeologists in search of ancient shipwrecks and drowned cities, oceanographers, chemists, physicists, geologists, biologists, will give a hundred jobs to dolphins, such as collecting data, measurements, samples and so on which are quite unobtainable today.

This, again, is not anticipation, not even prediction, just updating, for there it involves nothing new in the sunless world beneath the sea. We speak of aquanauts, but in time past it was the fishermen who enlisted dolphins in their aid. We have forgotten this but they have been helping the fishermen to fish for well over two thousand years.

169

Pliny the Elder, who about the year A.D. 70 was Procurator of Gallia Narbonensis (Provence), tells us how they went about it:

In the region of Nîmes, there is a marsh named Latera where dolphins catch fish in partnership with human fishermen. At a regular season a countless shoal of mullet rushes out of the narrow mouth of the marsh into the sea, after watching for the turn of the tide, which makes it impossible for nets to be spread across the channel – indeed the nets would be equally incapable of standing the mass of the weight even if the craft of the fish did not watch for the opportunity. For a similar reason they make straight out into the deep water produced by the nearby eddies, and hasten to escape from the only place suitable for setting nets. When this is observed by the fishermen – and a crowd collects at the place, because of their keenness for this sport – and when the entire population from the shore shouts as loud as it can, calling for 'Snubnose', for the *dénouement* of the show, the dolphins quickly hear their wishes ... and they suddenly hasten to the spot, in order to give their aid. Their line of battle comes into view, and at once deploys in the place where they are to join battle; they bar the passage on the side of the sea and drive the scared mullet into the shallows. Then the fishermen put their nets round them and lift them out of the water with forks. Nonetheless some frenzied mullets leap over the obstacles: but these are caught by the dolphins, which are satisfied for the time being with merely having killed them, postponing a meal till victory is won. The action is hotly contested, and the dolphins pressing on with the greatest bravery are delighted to be caught in the nets, and for fear that this itself may hasten the enemy's flight, they glide out between the boats and the nets or the swimming fishermen so gradually as not to open ways of escape; none of them try to get away by leaping out of the water, which otherwise they are very fond of doing, unless the nets are put below them. ... When in this way the catch has been completed they tear in pieces the fish that they have killed. But as they are aware that they have had too strenuous a task for only a single day's pay, they wait there till the following day, and are given a feed of bread mash dipped in wine, in addition to the fish.

In Euboea, Oppian observed a different *modus operandi* among the Greek fishermen:

When the fishers hasten to the toil of evening fishing, carrying to the fishes the menace of fire, even the swift gleam of the brazen lantern, the dolphins attend them, speeding the slaughter of their common prey. Then the fishes in terror turn away and seek escape, but the dolphins from the outer sea rush together upon them and frighten them and, when they would fain turn to the deep sea, they drive them forth towards the unfriendly land, leaping at them ever and again, even as dogs chasing the wild beast for the hunters and answering bark with bark. And when the fishes flee close to the land, the fishermen easily smite them with the well-pronged trident.

And there is no way of escape for them, but they dance about in the sea, driven by the fire and by the dolphins, the kings of the sea. But when the work of capture is happily accomplished, then the dolphins draw near and ask the guerdon of their friendship, even their allotted portion of the spoil. And the fishers deny them not, but gladly give them a share of their successful fishing; for if a man sins against them in his greed, no more are the dolphins his helpers in fishing.

Pliny saw the same night fishing practised at Iasos, with lights and dolphins. It was still going on in the sixteenth century:

The reason wherefore the dolphins be so beloved of the fishers is this: it is because they drive the fish together from every quarter into their nets. And for that they have their recompense, for the fishers never do them any harm. And even if they find them fast in their nets, yet they set them at liberty. I do not mean thereby that this is so in all seas but principally in Greece and those parts the inhabitants whereof eat no dolphins.

A friend of mine, a Greek born in the Sporades Islands, assures me that his great-uncle still goes fishing there today, in exactly the same way.

In Australia, on the coast of Queensland, at Moreton Bay, there is a little promontory called Amity Point. The aborigines, like many peoples of the Pacific, look on the dolphin with respect on account of its magical powers and also no doubt on account of the good turns which it does them. An account of the help dolphins give in fishing by the Director of Queensland Museum was given nearly a hundred years ago (I quote from Antony Alpers, who had it from the present director of the museum, who had it from a certain Fairholm writing in the

Transactions of the Zoological Society of Queensland for 1856):

Near Amity Point, some of the natives may constantly be found during the warmer months of the year fishing for mullet. In this pursuit they are assisted in a most wonderful manner by the porpoises. It seems that from time immemorial a sort of understanding has existed between the blacks and the porpoises for their mutual advantage, and the former pretend to know all the porpoises about the spot, and even have names for them.

The beach here consists of shelving sand, and near the shore are small hillocks of sand, on which the blacks sit, watching for the appearance of a shoal of mullet. Their nets, which are used by hand, and are stretched on a frame about four feet wide, lie ready on the beach. On seeing a shoal, several of the men run down, and with their spears make a peculiar splashing in the water. The porpoises being outside the shoal, numbers of the fish are secured before they can break away. In the scene of apparent confusion that takes place, the blacks and the porpoises are seen splashing about close to each other. So fearless are the latter that strangers, who have expressed doubts as to their tameness, have often been shown that they will take a fish from the end of a spear, when held to them.

For my part I cannot doubt that the understanding is real, and that the natives know these porpoises, and that strange porpoises would not show so little fear of the natives. The oldest men of the tribe say that the same kind of fishing has always been carried on as long as they can remember. Porpoises abound in the bay, but in no other part do the natives fish with their assistance.

There are too many other descriptions of this practice, all perfectly serious and consistent, for one to doubt the story. Another account adds:

The cooperative principle was so well understood between these fellow-adventurers, that an unsuccessful porpoise would swim backwards and forwards on the beach, until a friend from the shore waded out with a fish for him on the end of a spear.

And another witness:

I remember witnessing a great scene of fun and excitement at Amity Point. A large school of mullet were coming in along the shore, but were too far out in the deep water for the blacks, when a number of porpoises were observed rolling about five hundred yards away, and sunning themselves, in complete unawareness of the feast so near them. One black fellow went down to the beach with a spear, which he prodded into the sand several times, and then struck the water with it at full length horizontally. Instantly, the porpoises answered the signal, by dashing in, and, of course, driving the poor mullet before them, when there was a rush of about twenty natives into them with their nets and for the next two minutes nothing was to be seen but a confused mass of fish, porpoises and blacks, all mixed up together, out of which the blacks emerged with their nets as full as they could hold, and left the balance of the school to be taken care of by their curious allies.

Fresh-water dolphins have also formed the same sort of association with the fishermen of lakes and rivers. In the Chinese province of Yunnan, each family or each village had its own dolphin, *Lipotes vexillifer*, which must not be induced to drive the fish towards the nets of another family under penalty of law.

In India, for the past three thousand years, fishermen have been catching dolphins which they train to 'beat' the fish up to their nets. They train them when they are still young and keep them for the whole of their lives.

In the Upper Amazon basin, where the borders of Brazil, Colombia and Peru run together, the Boutus (*Inia geoffrensis*) are 'sacred dolphins', respected by the Indians as much as the common dolphin was by the Hellenes of old. They believe that he who lights his house with a candle of Boutu fat will be instantly stricken blind.

The most trustworthy account of these animals was published in the American magazine *Natural History* in 1954. It is by Bruce Lamb, an American agricultural expert who worked in Brazil for a long time. He had read neither Pliny nor Oppian, and neither had the Indians of Rio Tapajos, but he picked up from the lips of the natives testimony which once more confirms what we have gathered from many other sources. On several occasions the Boutus have saved the lives of Indian fishermen by pushing them ashore when their canoes had capsized in the great river; a playful dolphin had formed the habit of carrying off a fisherman's paddle between his teeth whenever he could grab it, and – this is worth noting – when the Boutus are about, the Indians can bathe or swim across a river without fear, for the piranhas fear and avoid the dolphins, which sometimes feed on them. Lamb has also personally seen *Inia* dolphins playing around a small river steamer and disappearing as though at a given signal at the precise moment when one of the stokers came on deck with a rifle and malice aforethought.

He tells another story too. One evening at nightfall he set off fishing in a canoe with one paddler and his guide Raymundo. As they went along the paddler began to knock gently against the gunwale, whistling at the same time at a special pitch, which Raymundo explained by saying that he was calling up 'their' dolphin, for he declared that they had a dolphin trained to react when summoned by coming to help them fish. Arriving at the fishing spot along the bank of the river, Raymundo lit a carbide lamp and chose a harpoon. Almost at once a dolphin appeared some fifteen yards away and 'blew'. 'Here we go,' said Raymundo. The canoe noiselessly coasted past the bank. Raymundo, in the prow, harpooned the fish, which were easily visible in the shallow water. Lamb says: 'As we progressed, the fish scattered ahead of us and went for deep water, but there they encountered our friend the dolphin, who was also fishing, and so they came rushing back to the shallows. Several times they sped back so fast they ended up flopping on the beach.' The catch was quite a good one. Raymundo decided to cross the river to try another spot. This took a quarter of an hour, and now Lamb could not see the dolphin surfacing every thirty seconds to breathe. 'It is because we are not going fast enough,' said Raymundo. 'He will be waiting for us over there, at the other fishing place.'

And when they got to it there was the dolphin. They resumed the same style of fishing, the men pushing the fish towards the dolphin and the dolphin driving them back towards the men.

'The Boutu', Lamb recalls, 'actually accompanied us at fifty to a hundred feet for over an hour. This differed greatly from the random feeding movements I have seen dolphins engage in on other occasions.'

But what of sailors, and submariners? If one day we get to

the point of talking to whales in all the languages of the liquid world, or in some interspecies Esperanto, or even on our fingers in deaf and dumb talk, that would be the end of all our navigational problems. For whales have no need of compasses or sextants, nor charts, nor clear weather, nor loglines nor chronometers, to find their way about the seas. Whalers and coastwise people have long known that dolphins, sperm whales and right whales have always followed the same routes on their annual migrations towards the hunting grounds where food abounds or to the chosen place of their mating. So all a captain lost in the fog would have to do would be to politely ask the first dolphin he met for his position and what course to steer. And before venturing into a dangerous strait he would just hail a pilot whale to guide him between the reefs and avoid the shoals.

There is nothing Utopian here either, nor, to be sure, anything very novel. Ever since Apollo turned himself into a dolphin to lead the Cretans lost in the tempest towards Crissa and safety, the real dolphins have kept up the habit. There are a score of examples in mythology, and the Greeks worshipped Apollo at the shrine of Delphi where those Cretan sailors first came ashore. There was another temple to Delphinian Apollo at Athens, built after a similar sea rescue.

More recently Commandant Cousteau himself has been able to establish the efficacy of pilot-dolphins. One day the research vessel *Elie Monnier* was steaming at eighteen knots in the Atlantic, towards the Straits of Gibraltar. She caught up with, and then passed, a school of dolphins who were obviously bound for the straits also. Forty miles off the Straits, Cousteau changed course very gradually by five or six degrees, trying to mislead them. The dolphins did the same, but after a few minutes corrected their error and pointed straight between the Pillars of Hercules.

Why not equip sailors and flying crew with a special transmitter which will automatically broadcast under water a recording of the dolphin distress signal? In case of shipwreck all the dolphins within range would come to the rescue, as in Aesop's fable.

What could be done about bathers? As it happens, they are

175

being dealt with. There is a holiday beach in South Africa now, where two female dolphins are in training. They are called Dimple and Haig, and if present progress continues, they will become fully qualified municipal beachmasters. If a swimmer gets into difficulties it will be up to them to bring him a life-buoy, and if a shark is signalled they will put off to intercept it.

Professor Taylor, who started this experiment, is convinced that in a few years' time the system will become general, probably using females only, for it seems that in them the rescue behaviour is most deeply ingrained.

But what advantage will this partnership, so profitable to man, have for the dolphins? In exchange for all the good turns that have been done them over thousands of years, and for all those that are to come in the future, what has humanity to offer to dolphins and to larger whales?

In Norway they have been diligently massacred for the last 9,000 years, as rock drawings show; in Sakhalin for 6,000 years; in Asia for 3,500 years (it is written in the *Rig Vedas*) and, according to Assyrian texts, for well over 3,000 years.

The dolphin of Hippo perished by the hand of niggardly citizens who were tired of contributing to the municipal fund to treat and lodge all the visiting V.I.P.s who came to see the famous animal.

In the very time of Aristotle certain barbarians hunted the dolphin 'catching them by means of noise,' and he added by way of explanation 'for violent noises stun them' – a statement treated by the ignorants of today with incredulous scorn. As it is, it is they who are wrong, for there are still barbarians in the world. For instance, the people of Va-Pan Island, in the Marquesas, are a disgrace to Polynesia where in general the dolphin is duly venerated. But then it should be borne in mind that the men of Va-Pan, if not anthropophagous themselves, are the sons and grandsons of cannibals. They ate their last missionary in 1910.

When meat is wanted for a feast about twenty canoes put off and keep a look-out. Edoardo Beccaro, an Italian journalist, has been on one of these hunts. When they see the fins of the dolphins on the surface, the canoes fan out, and then at a signal from the chief one man in each canoe takes two stones about the size of a coconut and knocks them violently together under water. For the dolphins with their delicate hearing this noise seems intolerably painful. They panic immediately, trying to make for the open sea. But their way is barred by the circle of canoes with their apocalyptic din. They tumble about, leap out of the water, as far away as they can, but now the only way lies inshore, towards a bay into which the canoes with their intolerable, painful acoustic goad are herding them. The boats come nearer, the sound shock of the stones beats on inexorably, the dolphins are terrified, but still the din comes nearer. Some of them try to keep their heads above water, with eyes closed, blood streaming from their ears and emitting a whistling asthmatic breath. They seem to be choking. Now the fearful sound overtakes them and is right among them. The dolphins lose consciousness, they are paralysed, they are 'stupefied with noise'.

Then the yelling men leap into the water, machete in hand. And the butchery begins.

Since the Middle Ages French guilds called 'Pêcheurs Réunis' or 'Societates Walmannorum', using great nets called 'madragues', have methodically organized the massacre of porpoises. Off the entire coast of Normandy the local authorities used to farm out sections of shore waters to syndicates of whalers called *Walmanni*, a Germanic or possibly Scandinavian, not Latin or Gallic term, probably indicating that this form of marine hunting was brought to Gaul by the Vikings or by the Saxons of the Orne estuary; in any case by barbarians!

Ironically the French themselves had made the dolphin 'the first in nobility after the lily', but Belon, almost in the same breath, tells us that the dolphin

is sovereign among the meats of France on fast days ... for brought to the fish market they are but destined to grace the tables of the rich, or else of those who for once are ready to make a great expense; for delicate eaters who have the most discerning taste have pronounced this meat to be the most delicious of all that swims ... for the dolphin or goose-beak is not so grossly fat as the porpoise and is of better flavour and of much more profit and delight ... it was the custom aforetime to throw away the two wings or arms of the dolphin together with the tails, and those also of porpoises, or to nail them over the doorway. But I know not what novelty has brought it about that nowadays these are preferred above all other parts of the fish, and this matter I learned at Rouen.

He also enlightens us about a sport much followed in the sixteenth century:

Sometimes they strike the dolphin with shots from an arbalest or an harquebus at sea, or else with pikes; yet they come not within the grasp of them that so strike them. Which thing is done but rarely, and then only in times of calm weather when the mariners have leisure enough and to spare, not knowing whither to turn for pastime.

In this same period the Italians gave the harpoon another name, calling it the *delfiniera*.

Ever since the seventeenth century in April or May when the porpoises run into the Baltic through the Sound in pursuit of shoals of herring, or out of it by the Little Belt, they fall into the toils of the great Scandinavian fisheries. In the nineteenth century the catch was a thousand or fifteen hundred every year.

The dolphin fisheries off Cape Hatteras or Long Island in the United States have not been long extinct, and in the Gulf of St Lawrence near Petite Rivière dolphin fishers are still in business.

In the Black Sea, down to a few years ago, the Sukhum dolphineers were killing two or three thousand annually between December and March.

From time to time, also, the newspapers publish pictures of a spear-fisherman who has responded to the friendly advances of some dolphin by shooting it in the head with a harpoon gun; the caption usually congratulates the 'intrepid Nimrod' or the 'fearless diver'.

Thus does man treat others of his friends: his most noble conquest the horse, praised by poets, sung in a thousand tributes of love, often ends as Belgian beefsteak. The dog, his best and oldest animal friend, is eaten at the first sign of famine or dispatched when the family moves to a new apartment house.

The most brilliant example of this candid, or should we say

monstrous, egoism is to be found in *Moby Dick*. Here is Herman Melville describing, apparently with love, the delightful Pacific beaked dolphin:

He always swims in hilarious shoals, which upon the broad sea keep tossing themselves to heaven like caps in a Fourth-of-July crowd. Their appearance is generally hailed with delight by the mariner. Full of fine spirits, they invariably come from the breezy billows to windward. They are the lads that always live before the wind. They are accounted a lucky omen. If you yourself can withstand three cheers at beholding these vivacious fish, then heaven help ye; the spirit of godly gamesomeness is not in ye.

A moving, a comforting description, isn't it? One feels oneself brought back to the great days of Greece. Well, just a minute, for on the very same line, Melville goes on:

A well-fed, plump Huzza Porpoise will yield you one good gallon of good oil. But the fine and delicate fluid extracted from his jaws is exceedingly valuable. It is in request among jewellers and watch-makers. Porpoise meat is good eating, you know.

Men began by killing the smaller cetacea, the porpoises and dolphins, because it was easier without large boats; although at least as early as the eleventh century, Basque whalers of the Bay of Biscay killed what later came to be called right whales. (They are of medium size and they float when dead, whence they were 'right' for the purpose.) But progress was coming; all species could be killed once it was possible to inflate the carcass of the 'wrong' whales with compressed air, and in our twentieth century, with air reconnaissance, radar, sonar and other mechanized aids, industrialized extermination is accelerated much faster than it can be slowed down by international agreement. Now if the whalers hunt only the giant whales, this is only because it is not economic to kill the smaller species. For the moment these are safe, but the situation can change again. Progress will not be denied. In proof of this the Department of Fisheries of Newfoundland is suggesting the decoying of pilot whales by means of their own distress signals, recorded on tape and played back under water, so as to lure them to destruction in narrow coves.

As for the scientific gentlemen who sacrifice dolphins by the dozens in their laboratories, they do this because, as one of them has said: 'Our responsibility [*sic*] lies in the pursuit of truth.' Not for the pleasures of the table do they rob the dolphin of his life, but purely for their pleasure of learning.

And as for me? Here I am, deploring and castigating the actions of naval officers and oil refiners, and almost excusing that of scientists. But am I not about to prepare and encourage yet another exploitation of the dolphin by man? Worse still, while preaching altruism, the same thought has been at the back of my mind this last fifteen years or so, ever since I took up diving:

The first thing I shall ask a dolphin, once I can speak to him, is to lead me to the wreck of some galleon loaded to the gunwales with gold and jewellery, beginning with that of the *Santo Cristo de Maracaibo* which belonged to the 1702 *Plata Flota*, lost in Vigo Bay, in Spain; I spent two years looking for her in vain.

As for the interspecies association, I have no real fears for the dolphins. They are clever enough to withdraw from it the moment they begin to be over-exploited, leaving their frustrated masters in the lurch.

But what of the murderers? If this book shall have contributed only a very little to making the weapons drop from their hands, then I think I shall sleep sounder.

We protect wild animals poorly, too little, and with scandalous weakness if any sort of short-sighted commercial interest is in the way. It is in our own interest as men to step up these protective measures, and I should like to make plain to a certain audience that in destroying nature, and the plants and animals which inhabit this globe, they are sawing off the branch on which they sit. If civilization ends by exterminating all that is wild and free, the totally civilized human race will find themselves kings of a doleful desert, not only on dry land but in the waters beneath, where life will no longer be worth living.

The case of marine mammals is more tragic still. In slaughtering our cousins, the dolphins, it is as if we were exterminating half-humans like the ape-man, the *Tropis* of Vercors.

In the Soviet Union the hunting and destruction of dolphins are today forbidden by law. This is the only country which up to the present has followed the great example set by the Greeks, the Polynesians and the Indians and, on two recent and limited occasions, by the Government of New Zealand. If Mr Alexander Ishkov, Minister of Fisheries, inaugurated this measure, he did it, so he declares, in the interests of science, and, in the words of Dr Sergei Kleinenberg, who has been working with dolphins for twelve years, 'because of the astounding attachment which they have towards men and because of the enormous potential which collaboration between dolphins and men in the sea could offer'.

So, what are they waiting for, all the other nations, to pass a bit of law reading 'Do not shoot the dolphins'?

10 Dolphin, Who Are You?

And so, dolphin, my friend, my cousin, who are you?

And what conclusion are we to draw from so much research and dissection, from so many opposing theories, from the torrents of experiments which make up that mass of scientific papers scattered on my desk and on the floor?

History and science have this in common, that they pass first through a stage of great confidence which slowly begins to waver, and soon dissolves as the work proceeds, and as new records accumulate with contradictory information.

It would be any historian's dream to be able to write the history of a battle based totally upon the memoirs of the winning general. But a historian is always a masochist, he gives himself the greatest inconveniences to complicate his task, he really tries harder, he ferrets about in every conceivable collection and archive, he strains his eyes deciphering old faded handwritings, he corresponds with a hundred other masochists like himself, he tracks down families, he turns upside-down the library basements, stirs up the dust in the depths of museums – until he finds the report of the losing general. Then he finds the one by the second-in-command and then the tale of the assistant to the Chief of Staff, the former's rival; the account of the trial of a traitor, the diaries of several eye-witnesses and then the testimony of the cook, and even the most biased version of the most obscure newspapers of the time – all these are turned up. Finally, when all these data are reviewed, the victory, which the original report described as a model of precision and organization, has become a blurred sequence of bloody events, full of confusion, of absurd orders and contradictions. A few more documents, and all the pieces begin to fit, everything is clarified: the victory was a defeat.

At what stage of the process are today's delphinologists? From their early works and spectacular results, some concluded with optimism: 'In ten years or less, we will talk to each other . . .' 'The world of the dolphin will be open to us . . .' Then came the stage of controversy. We are in the middle of it, but the day will come when enough contradictory information will be available, when enough experiments will have put enough data on each plateau of the balance to allow it to tilt it one way or the other. Will delphinology then become an outmoded fashion? A lost cause? And the dolphin? Will he be brought down to the level of the rabbit?

Or, will specialists redouble their efforts towards a goal which will then be regarded as unmistakably vital?

And if the latter, as I believe, as I hope, and as I know is true, will science, philosophy, and indeed our whole lives be profoundly changed by the contact, by the dialogue with an intelligent species that will open for us the doors of another universe?

Patience. The outcome still hangs in the balance.

Acknowledgements

Among the numerous delphinologists who have kindly helped him with up-to-date information and illustration material, the author would like to express his particular gratitude to Dr René-Guy Busnel, Director of the Animal Acoustic Laboratory in Juoy-en-Josas; Dr David H. Brown, Curator of Mammals at Marineland of the Pacific, Los Angeles; Mrs Karen W. Taylor and Mr A. Prior, Curator, Sea Life Park, and Chief Trainer, Oceanic Institute, Hawaii; Dr Murray A. Newman, Curator, Vancouver Public Aquarium; Mr William L. High, Fisheries Research Biologist, Seattle; Dr Lawrence Curtis, Director, Fort Worth Zoological Park; Mr and Mrs Roger Conklin of the Miami Seaquarium, and Adolf Frohn, Chief Trainer; Engineer Leo S. Balandis of Sperry Gyroscope Co.; Dr James N. Layne, Professor of Zoology, Cornell University, Ithaca, N.Y.; Dr David K. Caldwell, Curator, Marine Zoology, Los Angeles County Museum of Natural History; Colonel C. V. Glines, U.S.A.F., Director of the Information Service, Office of the Assistant Secretary of Defense; Mr Ricou Browning of the Ivan Tors Studios Inc.; and Dr S. David Webb, Assistant Curator of Natural Sciences, University of Florida.

The author would also like to thank Dr George F. Bond, Captain M.C., U.S. Navy, Special Projects Office, the father of the SEALAB project; as well as Mr. W. Leonov, Cultural Attaché to the U.S.S.R. Embassy in Brussels; the Director of Information Services of New Zealand in Wellington; Dr Tushingham of the Royal Ontario Museum in Toronto; the Curator of the Tunisia National Museums; the Trustees of the British Museum (Natural History) in London; the Head Curator, Mr George Konstantinopoulos, of the Archaeological Institute of the Dodecanese in Rhodes; Professor Augusto Traversa, Italian Institute of Culture in Brussels; and Captain Vichot, Curator of the Paris Maritime Museum.

Index

185

186

192